The Crystal Cabinet

HORACE GREGORY

AND MARYA ZATURENSKA

Holt, Rinehart and Winston / New York

The Crystal Cabinet

AN INVITATION TO POETRY

Wood engravings by Diana Bloomfield

*Grateful acknowledgment is made to the following publishers
and authors for permission to reprint copyrighted material:*

THE ATLANTIC MONTHLY for "Birthright" by John Drinkwater,
published in The Atlantic Monthly, September, 1916, and
copyrighted by The Atlantic Monthly.

THE BELKNAP PRESS of Harvard University Press for "The Wind
Begun to Rock the Grass" from *The Poems of Emily Dickinson,* edited by Thomas H. Johnson, copyright 1951, 1955 by
the President and Fellows of Harvard College; reprinted by
permission of the publishers and the Trustees of Amherst
College.

BASIL BUNTING for his translation of Lucretius' "Hymn to Venus"
from *Poems: 1950,* published by the Cleaner's Press of
Galveston, Texas.

JONATHAN CAPE, LIMITED, AND MRS. H. M. DAVIES for "Eardrops"
from *Collected Poems* by W. H. Davies, published in 1943 by
Jonathan Cape Limited.

THE CRESSET PRESS, LIMITED, for "The Viper" from *A Trophy of
Arms* by Ruth Pitter.

FOR GREGORY MONCURE, HOWELL CONWAY,
AND MARYA ANNE ZEIGLER.

We wish to extend our deep gratitude to Mrs. Dorothea Sinclair for help in preparing this manuscript; and to Patrick Bolton Gregory, Joanna Elizabeth Zeigler, Theresa de Kerpely, and Ann Durell for their editorial judgment, criticism, and advice.

Foreword

WE BELIEVE that "The Crystal Cabinet," the title of William Blake's strange and beautiful poem, conveys the feeling and atmosphere of this book. When we speak of feeling and atmosphere in this connection, we are actually saying that poetry has to do with insights and intuitions, and that these are stronger than reason. As Blake stood at the center of his Crystal Cabinet, he saw the tangible world magnified and made more wonderful than ever. The poem clarifies a moment of vision in which life becomes more terrifying and yet more beautiful than it was before. Although this heightened sense of life cannot be sustained, we perceive it best perhaps in the poetry of Blake, for surely he was a poet of great genius and imagination.

Poetry, like Heaven, has its many mansions; yet in this anthology we have been glad to find a setting for the rare poem—the poem of vision—that says in poetry all that can never be as well expressed in prose.

This book has a character that is all its own. We have made a point of choosing poems that have not appeared too frequently in other anthologies. Occasionally—but this is very seldom indeed—an extremely well-known poem does appear. The idea behind our selection is this: our book is an invitation to read poetry, to read it for pleasure, and ultimately to see the world with reawakened eyes. As we look around us, we shall also hear the music—often the immortal music—of poetry.

One of our hopes is that our readers will then turn to further discoveries in poetry, to books written by poets, to newly written poems as well as older ones (But a true poem is always new, and never old, no matter how long ago a poet wrote it!), and to poetry in other languages. The purpose of a good anthology is not to ask us to read anthologies forever, but is an invitation to learn more of the world that poets reveal to us; an invitation to find out more about individual poems and poets, and to guide us to the poets who most appeal to us.

Meanwhile, this book attempts to show some of the many ways in which a poem moves us, guiding us to moments of great joy in the world around us, or to the internal world of desires, riddles, and mysteries. While some poems are light-hearted, and others grave, we are certain that none are merely solemn or pretend to say more than they really mean. Since this book is for young readers of poetry, or for those who have taken up a rereading of poetry, we have not included long sustained and meditative poems—poems that are books in themselves—such as the great "Prelude" of Wordsworth, or Milton's "Samson Agonistes"—which are to be known and read and reread by mature readers. But "The Crystal Cabinet" does not close doors to the reading of longer poems. We hope that those very doors have been left wide open to further scenes and longer vistas.

Our selection of poems stresses the lyrical aspects of life and feeling, often reflecting moments of freshly inspired hopes and eagerness, and at another moment, intuitions of impending tragedy, or the arrow-like forethought of coming experience as in Yeats' fine love poem, "Brown Penny." Our choice has been in favor of the youthful emotions brought to life in Shakespeare's "Romeo and Juliet" rather than the mature passions in his rich yet complex "Anthony and Cleopatra."

> *Come and kiss me, sweet and twenty,*
> *Youth's a stuff t'will not endure*

are lines from his "Twelfth Night" that speak in the very spirit of the love poems in this book. Something of the same tuneful magic enters with "Chamber Music" by James Joyce:

> *Lean out of the window,*
> *Goldenhair.*

These words are modern, yet the atmosphere they create is of a youthfulness that is as timeless as the moonlit figure of Romeo at Juliet's balcony in old Verona.

As if the book were indeed a Crystal Cabinet, we find within it the refreshed and living themes of poetry: the variable face of Nature in changing seasons; the sunlit world as well as the mysteries of night; the contrasts of war and peace, of death and birth; the delights of riddling and nonsense. And in this book one also has a glimpse of ancient cities, old heroes—like Alexander come to life again—as well as the sight of modern city parks where boys and girls walk on a summer evening. In some of the poems we feel the presence of invisible, yet supernatural powers, of great good in contrast to violent evil. It is hoped that the readers of this book will find it a true journey to the essence of poetry. The doors of the Crystal Cabinet are open and all who wish to enter it are welcome.

HORACE GREGORY
MARYA ZATURENSKA

Contents

SECTION II

The Wind Begun to Rock the Grass

SECTION III

Musick, the Mosaique of the Air

SECTION IV

White Iope, Blithe Helen, and the Rest

SECTION V

We Were the Heroes

SECTION VI

How Many Heavens...

The Crystal Cabinet

The Crystal Cabinet

The Maiden caught me in the Wild,
Where I was dancing merrily;
She put me into her Cabinet,
And Lock'd me up with a golden Key.

This Cabinet is form'd of Gold
And Pearl and Crystal shining bright,
And within it opens into a World
And a little lovely Mooney Night.

Another England there I saw,
Another London with its Tower,
Another Thames and other Hills,
And another pleasant Surrey Bower,

Another Maiden like herself,
Translucent, lovely, shining clear,
Threefold each in the other clos'd,—
O, what a pleasant trembling fear!

O, what a smile! a threefold smile
Fill'd me, that like a flame I burn'd;
I bent to kiss the lovely Maid,
And found a Threefold Kiss return'd.

I strove to sieze the inmost Form
With ardour fierce and hands of flame,
But burst the Crystal Cabinet,
And like a Weeping Babe became—

A weeping Babe upon the wild,
A Weeping Woman pale reclin'd,
And in the outward air again
I fill'd with woes the passing Wind.

– William Blake

SECTION I

Sing We for Love

An Immortality

Sing we for love and idleness,
Naught else is worth the having.

Though I have been in many a land,
There is naught else in living.

And I would rather have my sweet,
Though rose-leaves die of grieving,

Than do high deeds in Hungary
To pass all men's believing.

— Ezra Pound

Doll's Boy's Asleep

Doll's boy's asleep
under a stile
he sees eight and twenty
ladies in a line

the first lady
says to nine ladies
his lips drink water
but his heart drinks wine

the tenth lady
says to nine ladies
they must chain his foot
for his wrist's too fine

the nineteenth
says to nine ladies
you take his mouth
for his eyes are mine.

Doll's boy's asleep
under the stile
for every mile the feet go
the heart goes nine

— *E. E. Cummings*

So Ghostly Then the Girl Came In

So ghostly then the girl came in
I never saw the turnstile twist
Down where the orchard trees begin
Lost in a reverie of mist.

And in the windless hour between
The last of daylight and the night,
When fields give up their ebbing green
And two bats interweave their flight,

I saw the turnstile glimmer pale
Just where the orchard trees begin,
But watching was of no avail,
Invisibly the girl came in.

I took one deep breath of the air
And lifted up my heavy heart;
It was not I who trembled there
But my immortal counterpart.

I knew that she had come again
Up from the orchard through the stile,
Without a sigh to tell me when,
Though I was watching all the while.

– *Robert Hillyer*

A Woman Driving

How she held up the horses' heads,
    Firm-lipped, with steady rein,
Down that grim steep the coastguard treads,
    Till all was safe again!

With form erect and keen contour
    She passed against the sea,
And, dipping into the chine's obscure,
    Was seen no more by me.

To others she appeared anew
    At times of dusky light,
But always, so they told, withdrew
    From close and curious sight.

Some said her silent wheels would roll
    Rutless on softest loam,
And even that her steeds' footfall
    Sank not upon the foam.

Where drives she now? It may be where
    No mortal horses are,
But in a chariot of the air
    Towards some radiant star.

– Thomas Hardy

Windy Nights

Whenever the moon and stars are set,
    Whenever the wind is high,
All night long in the dark and wet,
    A man goes riding by.
Late in the night when the fires are out,
    Why does he gallop and gallop about?

Whenever the trees are crying aloud,
    And ships are tossed at sea,
By, on the highway, low and loud,
    By at the gallop goes he.
By at the gallop he goes, and then
    By he comes back at the gallop again.

       – *Robert Louis Stevenson*

The Garden Seat

Its former green is blue and thin,
And its once firm legs sink in and in;
Soon it will break down unaware,
Soon it will break down unaware.

At night when reddest flowers are black
Those who once sat thereon come back;
Quite a row of them sitting there,
Quite a row of them sitting there.

With them the seat does not break down,
Nor winter freeze them, nor floods drown,
For they are as light as upper air,
They are as light as upper air!

— Thomas Hardy

Lydia Is Gone This Many a Year

Lydia is gone this many a year,
    Yet when the lilacs stir,
In the old gardens far or near,
    This house is full of her.

They climb the twisted chamber stair;
    Her picture haunts the room;
On the carved shelf beneath it there,
    They heap the purple bloom.

A ghost so long has Lydia been,
    Her cloak upon the wall,
Broidered, and gilt, and faded green,
    Seems not her cloak at all.

The book, the box on mantle laid,
    The shells in a pale row,
Are those of some dim little maid,
    A thousand years ago.

And yet the house is full of her;
    She goes and comes again;
And longings thrill, and memories stir,
    Like lilacs in the rain.

Out in their yards the neighbors walk,
   Among the blossoms tall;
Of Anne, of Phyllis do they talk,
   Of Lydia not at all.

— *Lizette Woodworth Reese*

Us Idle Wenches

It was a jolly bed in sooth,
    Of oak as strong as Babel.
And there slept Kit and Sall and Ruth
    As sound as maids are able.

Ay—three in one—and there they dreamed,
    Their bright young eyes hid under;
Nor hearkened when the tempest streamed
    Nor recked the rumbling thunder.

For marvellous regions strayed they in,
    Each moon—far from the other—
Ruth in her childhood, Kit in heaven,
    And Sall with ghost for lover.

But soon as ever sun shone sweet,
    And birds sang, praise for rain, O—
Leapt out of bed three pair of feet
    And danced on earth again, O!

– Anonymous

13

I Know Where I'm Going

I know where I'm going.
I know who's going with me,
I know who I love,
But the dear knows who I'll **marry**.

I'll have stockings of silk,
Shoes of fine green leather,
Combs to buckle my braid,
And a ring for every finger.

Feather beds are soft,
Painted rooms are bonny;
But I'd leave them all
To go with my love Johnny.

Some say he's dark,
I say he's bonny,
He's the flower of them all,
My handsome, coaxing Johnny.

I know where I'm going,
I know who's going with me,
I know who I love,
But the dear knows who I'll marry.

— *Anonymous*

For Anne Gregory

'Never shall a young man,
Thrown into despair
By those great honey-coloured
Ramparts at your ear,
Love you for yourself alone
And not your yellow hair.'

'But I can get a hair-dye
And set such colour there,
Brown, or black, or carrot,
That young men in despair
May love me for myself alone
And not my yellow hair.'

'I heard an old religious man
But yesternight declare
That he had found a text to prove
That only God, my dear,
Could love you for yourself alone
And not your yellow hair.'

— *William Butler Yeats*

Eardrops

This bag of cherries for my Love:
    She takes one lovely Pair,
And makes an eardrop of each one,
    To fit in either ear.
Until I swear it seems to me,
    To see those Cherry stones,
They almost match in loveliness
    The flesh that's on her bones.
They match her eyes in light and size,
    With such a glowing stain—
That every precious pearl is hurled
    Back to its sea again!

                    – *W. H. Davies*

An Old Song Ended

'How should I your true love know
    From another one?'
'By his cockle-hat and staff
    And his sandal-shoon.'

'And what signs have told you now
    That he hastens home?'
'Lo! the spring is nearly gone,
    He is nearly come.'

'For a token there is nought,
    Say, that he should bring?'
'He will bear a ring I gave
    And another ring.'

'How may I, when he shall ask,
    Tell him who lies there?'
'Nay, but leave my face unveiled
    And unbound my hair.'

'Can you say to me some word
    I shall say to him?'
'Say I'm looking in his eyes
    Though my eyes are dim.'

        – Dante Gabriel Rossetti

Brown Penny

I whispered, 'I am too young.'
And then, 'I am not old enough';
Wherefore I threw a penny
To find out if I might love.
'Go and love, go and love, young man,
If the lady be young and fair.'
Ah, penny, brown penny, brown penny,
I am looped in the loops of her hair.

O love is the crooked thing,
There is nobody wise enough
To find out all that is in it,
For he would be thinking of love
Till the stars had run away
And the shadows eaten the moon.
Ah, penny, brown penny, brown penny,
One cannot begin it too soon.

— *William Butler Yeats*

TO Anthea WHO MAY COMMAND HIM ANY THING.

> Bid me to live, and I will live
>> Thy Protestant to be;
> Or bid me love, and I will give
>> A loving heart to thee.
>
> A heart as soft, a heart as kind,
>> A heart as sound and free
> As in the whole world thou canst find,
>> That heart Ile give to thee.
>
> Bid that heart stay, and it will stay
>> To honor thy Decree;
> Or bid it languish quite away,
>> And't shall do so for thee.
>
> Bid me to weep, and I will weep,
>> While I have eyes to see;
> And having none, yet will I keep
>> A heart to weep for thee.
>
> Bid me despaire, and Ile despaire,
>> Under that *Cypresse* tree;
> Or bid me die, and I will dare
>> E'en Death, to die for thee.

19

Thou art my life, my love, my heart,
   The very eyes of me;
And has command of every part,
   To live and die for thee.

— *Robert Herrick*

A Song From Cyprus

Where is the nightingale,
in what myrrh-wood and dim?
ah, let the night come black,
for we would conjure back
all that enchanted him,
    all that enchanted him.

Where is the bird of fire?
in what packed hedge of rose?
in what roofed ledge of flower?
no other creature knows
what magic lurks within,
    what magic lurks within.

Bird, bird, bird, bird, we cry,
hear, pity us in pain;
hearts break in the sunlight,
hearts break in the daylight rain,
only night heals again,
    only night heals again.

– H. D.

The River-Merchant's Wife:
A Letter

While my hair was still cut straight across my forehead
I played about the front gate, pulling flowers.
You came by on bamboo stilts, playing horse,
You walked about my seat, playing with blue plums.
And we went on living in the village of Chokan:
Two small people, without dislike or suspicion.

At fourteen I married My Lord you.
I never laughed, being bashful.
Lowering my head, I looked at the wall.
Called to, a thousand times, I never looked back.

At fifteen I stopped scowling,
I desired my dust to be mingled with yours
For ever and for ever and for ever.
Why should I climb the look out?

At sixteen you departed,
You went into far Ku-to-yen, by the river of swirling eddies,
And you have been gone five months.
The monkeys make sorrowful noise overhead.
You dragged your feet when you went out.

By the gate now, the moss is grown, the different mosses,
Too deep to clear them away!
The leaves fall early this autumn, in wind.
The paired butterflies are already yellow with August
Over the grass in the West garden;
They hurt me. I grow older.
If you are coming down through the narrows of the river
      Kiang,
Please let me know beforehand,
And I will come out to meet you,
As far as Cho-fu-Sa.

— Rihaku
TRANSLATED BY EZRA POUND

Louisa

I met Louisa in the shade,
And, having seen that lovely Maid,
Why should I fear to say
That, nymph-like, she is fleet and strong,
And down the rocks can leap along
Like rivulets in May?

She loves her fire, her cottage-home;
Yet o'er the moorland will she roam
In weather rough and bleak;
And, when against the wind she strains,
Oh! might I kiss the mountain rains
That sparkle on her cheek.

Take all that's mine "beneath the moon,"
If I with her but half a noon
May sit beneath the walls
Of some old cave, or mossy nook,
When up she winds along the brook
To hunt the waterfalls.

— *William Wordsworth*

An Apple Gathering

I plucked pink blossoms from mine apple-tree
    And wore them all that evening in my hair:
Then in due season when I went to see
    I found no apples there.

With dangling basket all along the grass
    As I had come I went the selfsame track:
My neighbours mocked me while they saw me pass
    So empty-handed back.

Lilian and Lilias smiled in trudging by,
    Their heaped-up basket teazed me like a jeer;
Sweet-voiced they sang beneath the sunset sky,
    Their mother's home was near.

Plump Gertrude passed me with her basket full,
    A stronger hand than hers helped it along;
A voice talked with her through the shadows cool
    More sweet to me than song.

Ah Willie, Willie, was my love less worth
    Than apples with their green leaves piled above?
I counted rosiest apples on the earth
    Of far less worth than love.

So once it was with me you stooped to talk
    Laughing and listening in this very lane;
To think that by this way we used to walk
    We shall not walk again!

I let my neighbours pass me, ones and twos
    And groups; the latest said the night grew chill,
And hastened: but I loitered; while the dews
    Fell fast I loitered still.

– Christina Rossetti

SECTION II

The Wind Begun to
Rock the Grass

The Wind Begun to Rock the Grass

The Wind begun to rock the Grass
With threatening Tunes and low—
He threw a Menace at the Earth—
A Menace at the Sky.

The Leaves unhooked themselves from Trees—
And started all abroad
The Dust did scoop itself like Hands
And threw away the Road.

The Wagons quickened on the Streets
The Thunder hurried slow—
The Lightning showed a Yellow Beak
And then a livid Claw.

The Birds put up the Bars to Nests—
The Cattle fled to Barns—
Then came one drop of Giant Rain
And then as if the Hands

That held the Dams had parted hold
The Waters Wrecked the Sky,
But overlooked my Father's House—
Just quartering a Tree—

— *Emily Dickinson*

Stars Wheel in Purple

Stars wheel in purple, yours is not so rare
as Hesperus, nor yet so great a star
as bright Aldebaran or Sirius,
nor yet the stained and brilliant one of War;

stars turn in purple, glorious to the sight;
yours is not gracious as the Pleiades are
nor as Orion's sapphires, luminous;

yet disenchanted, cold, imperious face,
when all the others blighted, reel and fall,
your star, steel-set, keeps lone and frigid tryst
to freighted ships, baffled in wind and blast.

– H. D.

The Spring

Now that winter's gone, the earth hath lost
Her snow-white robes; and now no more the frost
Candies the grass, or casts an icy cream
Upon the silver lake or crystal stream;
But the warm sun thaws the benumbed earth,
And makes it tender; gives a sacred birth
To the dead swallow; wakes in hollow tree
The drowsy cuckoo and the humble-bee.
Now do a choir of chirping minstrels bring,
In triumph to the world, the youthful Spring:
The vallies, hills, and woods, in rich array,
Welcome the coming of the long'd-for May.

Now all things smile; only my love doth lower;
Nor hath the scalding noon-day sun the power
To melt that marble ice, which still doth hold
Her heart congeal'd, and makes her pity cold.
The ox, which lately did for shelter fly
Into the stall, doth now securely lie
In open fields; and love no more is made
By the fire-side; but, in the cooler shade,
Amyntas now doth with his Chloris sleep
Under a sycamore, and all things keep
Time with the season—only she doth carry
June in her eyes, in her heart January.

– *Thomas Carew*

The Return of Spring

Now Time throws off his cloak again
Of ermined frost, and wind, and rain,
And clothes him in the embroidery
Of glittering sun and clear blue sky.
With beast and bird the forest rings,
Each in his jargon cries or sings;
And Time throws off his cloak again
Of ermined frost, and wind, and rain.

River, and fount, and tinkling brook
Wear in their dainty livery
Drops of silver jewelry;
In new-made suit they merry look;
And Time throws off his cloak again
Of ermined frost, and wind, and rain

— *Charles D'Orleans*
TRANSLATED BY
HENRY WADSWORTH LONGFELLOW

Song

Once my heart was a summer rose
That cares not for right or wrong,
And the sun was another rose, that year,
They shone, the sun and the rose, my dear—
Over the long and the light summer land
All the bright summer long.

As I walked in the long and the light summer land,
All that I knew of shade
Was the cloud, my ombrelle of rustling gray
Sharp silk, it had spokes of gray steel rain—
Hiding my rose away, my dear,
Hiding my rose away.

And my laughter shone like a flight of birds
All in the summer gay—
Tumbling pigeons and chattering starlings
And other pretty darlings, my dear,
And other pretty darlings.

To my heart like a rose, a rain of tears
(All the bright summer long)
Was only the sheen on a wood-dove's breast,
And sorrow only her song, my love—
And sorrow only my rest.

I passed a while in Feather Town—
(All the bright summer long)—
The idle wind puffed that town up
In air, then blew it down.

I walk alone now in Lead Town
(All in the summer gay . . .)
Where the steady people walk like the Dead—
And will not look my way.

For, withering my heart, that summer rose,
Came another heart like a sun—
And it drank all the dew from the rose, my love,
And the birds have forgotten their song
That sounded all summer long, my dear—
All the bright summer long.

— *Dame Edith Sitwell*

High Summer

The ground is hard, and o'er the fallows now
The boys are forced to lean upon the plough;
The ground is full of cracks and gapes for wet,
And cobwebs hang on all the bushes met.
The snakes lie beaking where the waters play
And make the maiden almost faint away.
The idle boy sits on the brigs at play
And keeps a bough to knock the flies away;
And ever followed by a lazy dog,
He wades the flaggy dyke and pelts the frog
And gets the great brier balls and likes them well
And crops the coddled apples for the smell
And fills his hands among the poppied corn
With pleasant weeds that scent the gales of morn.

– John Clare

Two Rivers

Thy summer voice, Musketaquit,
Repeats the music of the rain;
But sweeter rivers pulsing flit
Through thee, as thou through Concord Plain.

Thou in thy narrow banks art pent:
The stream I love unbounded goes
Through flood and sea and firmament;
Through light, through life, it forward flows.

I see the inundation sweet,
I hear the spending of the stream
Through years, through men, through Nature fleet,
Through love and thought, through power and dream.

Musketaquit, a goblin strong,
Of shard and flint makes jewels gay;
They lose their grief who hear his song,
And where he winds is the day of day.

So forth and brighter fares my stream,—
Who drink it shall not thirst again;
No darkness stains its equal gleam,
And ages drop in it like rain.

– *Ralph Waldo Emerson*

Ruth

She stood breast high among the corn,
Clasp'd by the golden light of morn,
Like the sweetheart of the sun,
Who many a glowing kiss had won.

On her cheek an autumn flush,
Deeply ripen'd;—such a blush
In the midst of brown was born,
Like red poppies grown with corn.

Round her eyes her tresses fell,
Which were blackest none could tell,
But long lashes veil'd a light
That had else been all too bright.

And her hat, with shady brim,
Made her tressy forehead dim;
Thus she stood among the stooks,
Praising God with sweetest looks:

Sure, I said, heav'n did not mean
Where I reap thou shoudst but glean,
Lay thy sheaf adown and come,
Share my harvest and my home.

— *Thomas Hood*

In Shadow

Out in the late amber afternoon,
Confused among chrysanthemums,
Her parasol, a pale balloon,
Like a waiting moon, in shadow swims.

Her furtive lace and misty hair
Over the garden dial distill
The sunlight,—then withdrawing, wear
Again the shadows at her will.

Gently yet suddenly, the sheen
Of stars inwraps her parasol.
She hears my step behind the green
Twilight, stiller than shadows, fall.

"Come, it is too late,—too late
To risk alone the light's decline:
Nor has the evening long to wait,"—
But her own words are night's and mine.

– Hart Crane

Memory of Flowers

Felicity in the air
Carven of petals, living clearly
On pure light, precarious dew.
This is the scheme of the rose
And singing morning
Crystal over white pebbles in the pool.

You who remember
Know that the mind grows as foam upon flat waters
Harrowed by steel and wind.

And walk at dusk in tenantless places,
Hearing the hesitations of falling leaves;
Enter the misty spaces drained of summer,
Violet and gold of the dying autumn,
Cloaks of sunset light spilt dreaming in darkness
Over the trunks of trees.
You will not fear the winter.
Dimensions in the sky will not oppress you,
Sorrow, nor sequences of days.

If you will,
Take up this other loveliness;
Pale women darkly gowned
Walk slowly in the gardens
In the autumnal forest
In the evening air.

        – Robert Fitzgerald

October

O hushed October morning mild,
Thy leaves have ripened to the fall;
Tomorrow's wind, if it be wild,
Should waste them all.
The crows above the forest call;
Tomorrow they may form and go.
O hushed October morning mild,
Begin the hours of this day slow.
Make the day seem to us less brief.
Hearts not averse to being beguiled,
Beguile us in the way you know.
Release one leaf at break of day;
At noon release another leaf;
One from our trees, one far away.
Retard the sun with gentle mist;
Enchant the land with amethyst.
Slow, slow!
For the grapes' sake, if they were all,
Whose leaves are already burnt with frost,
Whose clustered fruit must else be lost—
For the grapes' sake along the wall.

– Robert Frost

Poem
in October

It was my thirtieth year to heaven
Woke to my hearing from harbour and neighbour wood
   And the mussel pooled and the heron
      Priested shore
     The morning beckon
With water praying and call of seagull and rook
And the knock of sailing boats on the net webbed wall
    Myself to set foot
     That second
   In the still sleeping town and set forth.

My birthday began with the water—
Birds and the birds of the winged trees flying my name
   Above the farms and the white horses
     And I rose
    In rainy autumn
And walked abroad in a shower of all my days.
High tide and the heron dived when I took the road
    Over the border
     And the gates
   Of the town closed as the town awoke.

A springful of larks in a rolling
Cloud and the roadside bushes brimming with whistling
    Blackbirds and the sun of October
        Summery
    On the hill's shoulder,
Here were fond climates and sweet singers suddenly
Come in the morning where I wandered and listened
    To the rain wringing
        Wind blow cold
    In the wood faraway under me.

Pale rain over the dwindling harbour
And over the sea wet church the size of a snail
    With its horns through mist and the castle
        Brown as owls
    But all the gardens
Of spring and summer were blooming in the tall tales
Beyond the border and under the lark full cloud.
    There could I marvel
        My birthday
    Away but the weather turned around.

It turned away from the blithe country
And down the other air and the blue altered sky
    Streamed again a wonder of summer
        With apples
    Pears and red currants
And I saw in the turning so clearly a child's

Forgotten mornings when he walked with his mother
    Through the parables
      Of sun light
And the legends of the green chapels

    And the twice told fields of infancy
That his tears burned my cheeks and his heart moved in
        mine.
    These were the woods the river and sea
      Where a boy
    In the listening
Summertime of the dead whispered the truth of his joy
To the trees and the stones and the fish in the tide.
    And the mystery
      Sang alive
Still in the water and singing birds.

    And there I could marvel my birthday
Away but the weather turned around. And the true
    Joy of the long dead child sang burning
      In the sun.
    It was my thirtieth
Year to heaven stood there then in the summer noon
Though the town below lay leaved with October blood.
    O may my heart's truth
      Still be sung
On this high hill in a year's turning.

* – Dylan Thomas*

The Walk

A walk above the waters' side,
None else to hearken there was come,
Where through haunt green and wellaway
I watched the low brook waters glide.
The heart rose stifling where it lay:
A voice dwelt there and was dumb.

The waters glided wellaway,
Hoarfast-hasting, jewel-swung;
And still that sound went breathing by
Of what they all at last would say;
An ear could overcatch the cry,
Though yet not all its tone was wrung.

The will shall learn itself alone,
For walking by the waters' side,
At every step my ear I bowed,
And heard from rift and runnelstone:
Away, they told delight aloud,
Away, it was the heart replied.

— *Léonie Adams*

Autumn

There is wind where the rose was;
Cold rain where sweet grass was;
    And clouds like sheep
    Stream o'er the steep
Grey skies where the lark was.

Nought gold where your hair was;
Nought warm where your hand was;
    But phantom, forlorn,
    Beneath the thorn,
Your ghost where your face was.

Sad winds where your voice was;
Tears, tears where my heart was;
    And ever with me,
    Child, ever with me,
Silence where hope was.

       — *Walter de la Mare*

The Christmas Robin

The snow of February had buried Christmas
Deep in the woods, where grew self-seeded
The fir-trees of a Christmas yet unknown,
Without a candle or a strand of tinsel.

Nevertheless when, hand in hand, plodding
Between the frozen ruts, we lovers paused
And 'Christmas trees!' cried suddenly together,
Christmas was there again, as in December.

We velveted our love with fantasy
Down a long vista-row of Christmas trees,
Whose coloured candles slowly guttered down
As grandchildren came drooping round our knees.

But he knew better, did the Christmas robin—
The murderous robin with his breast aglow
And legs apart, in a spade-handle perched:
He prophesied more snow, and worse than snow.

— *Robert Graves*

Phillis Inamorata

Come, be my valentine!
I'll gather eglantine,
Cowslips and sops-in-wine,
  With fragrant roses;
Down by thy Phillis sit,
She will white lilies get,
And daffadillies fit
  To make thee posies.

I bear, in sign of love,
A sparrow in my glove,
And in my breast a dove—
  This shall be all thine.
Besides, of sheep a flock,
Which yieldeth many a lock,
And this shall be thy stock—
  Come, be my valentine!

– *Dr. Lancelot Andrewes*

Kind Valentine

She hugs a white rose to her heart—
The petals flare—in her breath blown;
She'll catch the fruit on her death day—
The flower rooted in the bone.
The face at evening comes for love;
Reeds in the river meet below.
She sleeps small child, her face a tear;
The dream comes in with stars to go
Into the window, feigning snow.
This is the book that no one knows.
The paper wall holds mythic oaks,
Behind the oaks a castle grows.
Over the door, and over her
(She dies! she wakes!) the steeds gallop.

The child stirs, hits the dumb air, weeps,
Afraid of night's long loving-cup.

Into yourself, live,—Joanne!
And count the buttons—how they run
To doctor, red chief, lady's man!
Most softly pass, on the stairs down,
The stranger in your evening gown.
Hearing white, inside your grief,
An insane laughter up the roof.
O little wind, come in with dawn—
It is your shadow on the lawn.

Break the pot! and let carnations—
Smell them! they're the very first.
Break the sky and let come magic
Rain! Let earth come pseudo-tragic
Roses—blossom, unrehearsed.
Head, break! is broken. Dream, so small,
Come in to her. O little child,
Dance on squills where the winds run wild.

The candles rise in the warm night
Back and forth, the tide is bright.
Slowly, slowly, the waves retreat
Under her wish and under feet.
And over tight breath, tighter eyes,

The mirror ebbs, it ebbs and flows.
And the intern, the driver, speed
To gangrene! But—who knows—suppose
He was beside her! Please, star-bright,
First I see, while in the night
A soft-voiced, like a tear, guitar—
It calls a palm coast from afar.
And oh, so far the stars were there
For him to hang upon her hair
Like the white rose he gave, white hot,
While the low sobbing band—it wept
Violets and forget-me-nots.

— *David Schubert*

Garden Abstract

The apple on its bough is her desire,—
Shining suspension, mimic of the sun.
The bough has caught her breath up, and her voice,
Dumbly articulate in the slant and rise
Of branch on branch above her, blurs her eyes.
She is prisoner of the tree and its green fingers.

And so she comes to dream herself the tree,
The wind possessing her, weaving her young veins,
Holding her to the sky and its quick blue,
Drowning the fever of her hands in sunlight.
She has no memory, nor fear, nor hope
Beyond the grass and shadows at her feet.

– Hart Crane

The Red-Gold Rain

Sun and rain at work together
Ripened this for summer weather;
Sun gave it colour tawny red
And rain its life as though it bled;
In the long days full of fire
Its fruit will cool us when we tire.
Against the housewall does it grow
With smooth stem like a fountain's flow,
Dark are the leaves, a colder shade
Than ever rock or mountain made;
When the wind plays soft they sing,
From here the birds' songs never ring,
Quite still the fruit that in a golden shower
Will fall one day to flood this tower.

— *Sacheverell Sitwell*

Orange Tree by Night

If you feel for it pressing back the glossy leaves
The fruit looks cold as if its sullen fire is dying,
So red the ember that you scarcely dare to touch it:
And when your fingers close upon its moonlike rind
Chill must be the flavour like a hidden fountain
Whose waters sparkle springing clear from out the rock—
What are its leaves then, but wings, or the wind?—
Wings to hold the fruit high and cool it in the clouds,
Or wind blowing over those hot rocks that hold the water?

– Sacheverell Sitwell

Child's Song

FROM A MASQUE

I have a garden of my own,
>Shining with flowers of every hue;
I loved it dearly while alone,
>But I shall love it more with you:
And there the golden bees shall come,
>In summer-time at break of morn,
And wake us with their busy hum
>Around the Siha's fragrant thorn.

I have a fawn from Aden's land,
>On leafy buds and berries nurst;
And you shall feed him from your hand,
>Though he may start with fear at first.
And I will lead you where he lies
>For shelter from the noon-tide heat;
And you may touch his sleeping eyes,
>And feel his little silvery feet.

— *Thomas Moore*

Evening Waterfall

What was the name you called me?—
And why did you go so soon?

The crows lift their caw on the wind,
And the wind changed and was lonely.

The warblers cry their sleepy-songs
Across the valley gloaming,
Across the cattle-horns of early stars.

Feathers and people in the crotch of a treetop
Throw an evening waterfall of sleepy-songs.

What was the name you called me?—
And why did you go so soon?

– Carl Sandburg

SECTION III

Musick, the Mosaique of the Air

Musicks Empire

First was the world as one great cymbal made,
Where jarring windes to infant Nature plaid;
All Musick was a solitary sound,
To hollow rocks and murm'ring fountains bound.

Jubal first made the wilder notes agree;
And Jubal tuned Musicks Jubilee:
He call'd the echoes from their sullen cell,
And built the organs city where they dwell.

Each sought a consort in that lovely place;
And virgin trebles wed the manly base,
From whence the progeny of numbers new
Into harmonious colonies withdrew.

Some to the lute, some to the viol went,
And others chose the cornet eloquent.
These practising the wind, and those the wire,
To sing mens triumphs, or in Heavens quire.

Then Musick, the mosaique of the air,
Did all of these a solemn noise prepare:
With which she gain'd the empire of the ear,
Including all between the earth and sphear.

Victorious sounds! yet here your homage do
Unto a gentler conqueror than you;
Who though he flies the musick of his praise,
Would with you Heaven's hallelujahs raise.

– Andrew Marvell

Peter Quince at the Clavier

Just as my fingers on these keys
Make music, so the self-same sounds
On my spirit make a music too.

Music is feeling, then, not sound;
And thus it is that what I feel,
Here in this room, desiring you,

Thinking of your blue-shadowed silk,
Is music. It is like the strain
Waked in the elders by Susanna:

Of a green evening, clear and warm,
She bathed in her still garden, while
The red-eyed elders, watching, felt

The basses of their being throb
In witching chords, and their thin blood
Pulse pizzicati of Hosanna.

In the green water, clear and warm,
Susanna lay.
She searched
The touch of springs,
And found
Concealed imaginings.

She sighed
For so much melody.

Upon the bank she stood
In the cool
Of spent emotions.
She felt, among the leaves,
The dew
Of old devotions.

She walked upon the grass,
Still quavering.
The winds were like her maids,
On timid feet,
Fetching her woven scarves,
Yet wavering.

A breath upon her hand
Muted the night.
She turned—
A cymbal clashed,
And roaring horns.

III

Soon, with a noise like tambourines,
Came her attendant Byzantines.
They wondered why Susanna cried
Against the elders by her side:

And as they whispered, the refrain
Was like a willow swept by rain.

Anon their lamps' uplifted flame
Revealed Susanna and her shame.

And then the simpering Byzantines
Fled, with a noise like tambourines.

IV

Beauty is momentary in the mind—
The fitful tracing of a portal;
But in the flesh it is immortal.

The body dies; the body's beauty lives.
So evenings die, in their green going,
A wave, interminably flowing.

So gardens die, their meek breath scenting
The cowl of Winter, done repenting.
So maidens die to the auroral
Celebration of a maiden's choral.

Susanna's music touched the bawdy strings
Of those white elders; but, escaping,
Left only Death's ironic scraping.
Now in its immortality, it plays
On the clear viol of her memory,
And makes a constant sacrament of praise.

— *Wallace Stevens*

When to Her Lute Corinna Sings

FROM A BOOK OF AYRES

When to her lute Corinna sings,
Her voice revives the leaden stringes,
And doth in highest noates appeare,
As any challeng'd Eccho cleere;
But when she doth of mourning speake,
E'en with her sighs the strings do breake.

And as her lute doth live or die,
Led by her passion, so must I!
For when of pleasure she doth sing,
My thoughts enjoy a sudaine spring;
But if she doth of sorrow speake,
E'en from my heart the strings do breake.

— *Thomas Campion*

Sister, Awake!

Sister, awake! close not your eyes!
The day her light discloses,
And the bright morning doth arise
Out of her bed of roses.

See the clear sun, the world's bright eye,
In at our window peeping:
Lo, how he blusheth to espy
Us idle wenches sleeping!

Therefore awake! make haste, I say,
And let us, without staying,
All in our gowns of green so gay
Into the Park a-maying.

– Thomas Bateson

On Music

Many love music but for music's sake,
Many because her touches can awake
Thoughts that repose within the breast half-dead,
And rise to follow where she loves to lead.
What various feelings come from days gone by!
What tears from far-off sources dim the eye!
Few, when light fingers with sweet voices play
And melodies swell, pause, and melt away,
Mind how at every touch, at every tone,
A spark of life hath glistened and hath gone.

— *Walter Savage Landor*

The Reaper

Created by the poets to sing my song,
or created by my song to sing.

The source of the song must die away.

All day the night of music hovers
in the fir-tree, swims and glitters.
O touch me not to song
for I desire to be forever mute with my first Lord.

The source of the song will die away.

Glorious is the hot sun.
The reaper in his youth cuts down the living grain.
We see the glitter of his hot curved scythe.
His weary labours cut us down
while yet we live.

The source of the song will die away.

Sweep not upon the strings of my dark lyre,
my body, music; make mute
the tree within the heart, for I desire
to come unto my Lord unsung: the Tomb
of Muses in the marble of the flesh
is like a monument of song.

The source of the song will die away.

All night the pestilential reaper slays.
We fall away beneath his blade.
Our youth is daily harvested like wheat
from the fields of our first Lord.

The source of the song will die away.

But see, glorious is the hot sun.
The Reaper cuts my hot youth down.
He cuts me down from my first Lord
while yet I live.

The source of the song will die away.

— *Robert Duncan*

Song for Two Voices

'O Dionysus of the tree—you of the beard,
    you of the ripeness
Among the branches of my arms and hair
As the boughs of the vine hold the plane-tree—
You came like the wind in the branches.'

'And to the earth of my heart, O golden woman,
You are the corn-goddess.'

'O wind, come again to my branches.'

'O darkness of earth—O ripeness.'

               – *Dame Edith Sitwell*

Song

FROM THE BRIDES' TRAGEDY, ACT V, SCENE III

FIRST VOICE.

Who is the baby, that doth lie
Beneath the silken canopy
Of thy blue eye?

SECOND.

It is young Sorrow, laid asleep
In the crystal deep.

BOTH.

Let us sing his lullaby,
Heigho! a sob and a sigh.

FIRST VOICE.

What sound is that, so soft, so clear,
Harmonious as a bubbled tear
Bursting, we hear?

SECOND.

It is young Sorrow, slumber breaking,
Suddenly awaking.

BOTH.

Let us sing his lullaby,
Heigho! a sob and a sigh.

— Thomas Lovell Beddoes

From "Chamber Music"

V

Lean out of the window,
   Goldenhair,
I heard you singing
   A merry air.

My book was closed;
   I read no more,
Watching the fire dance
   On the floor.

I have left my book,
   I have left my room,
For I heard you singing
   Through the gloom.

Singing and singing
   A merry air,
Lean out of the window,
   Goldenhair.

– James Joyce

now (more near ourselves than we)

now (more near ourselves than we)
is a bird singing in a tree,
who never sings the same thing twice
and still that singing's always his

eyes can feel but ears may see
there never lived a gayer he;
if earth and sky should break in two
he'd make them one(his song's so true)

who sings for us for you for me
for each leaf newer than can be:
and for his own(his love)his dear
he sings till everywhere is here

— *E. E. Cummings*

The Song of the Mad Prince

Who said, 'Peacock Pie'?
    The old King to the sparrow:
Who said, 'Crops are ripe'?
    Rust to the harrow:
Who said, 'Where sleeps she now?
    Where rests now her head,
Bathed in eve's loveliness'?—
    That's what I said.

Who said, 'Ay, mum's the word';
    Sexton to willow:
Who said, 'Green dusk for dreams,
    Moss for a pillow'?
Who said, 'All Time's delight
    Hath she for narrow bed;
Life's troubled bubble broken'?—
    That's what I said.

– Walter de la Mare

White Iope, Blithe Helen,
and the Rest

When Thou Must Home
to Shades of Underground

FROM A BOOK OF AYRES

When thou must home to shades of underground,
And there ariv'd, a newe admired guest,
The beauteous spirits do engirt thee round,
White Iope, blithe Helen, and the rest,
To heare the stories of thy finisht love
From that smooth toong whose musicke hell can move;

Then wilt thou speake of banqueting delights,
Of masques and revels which sweete youth did make,
Of turnies and great challenges of knights,
And all these triumphs for thy beauties sake:
When thou hast told these honours done to thee,
Then tell, O tell, how thou didst murther me.

– Thomas Campion

Blue Girls

Twirling your blue skirts, travelling the sward
Under the towers of your seminary,
Go listen to your teachers old and contrary
Without believing a word.

Tie the white fillets then about your lustrous hair
And think no more of what will come to pass
Than bluebirds that go walking on the grass
And chattering on the air.

Practice your beauty, blue girls, before it fail;
And I will cry with my loud lips and publish
Beauty which all our power shall never establish,
It is so frail.

For I could tell you a story which is true:
I know a lady with a terrible tongue,
Blear eyes fallen from blue,
All her perfections tarnished—and yet it is not long
Since she was lovelier than any of you.

– John Crowe Ransom

Sonnet cvi

When in the chronicle of wasted time
I see descriptions of the fairest wights,
And beauty making beautiful old rime,
In praise of Ladies dead and lovely Knights;
Then, in the blazon of sweet beauty's best,
Of hand, of foot, of lip, of eye, of brow,
I see their antique pen would have exprest
Even such a beauty as you master now.
So all their praises are but prophecies
Of this our time, all you prefiguring;
And, for they look'd but with divining eyes,
They had not skill enough your worth to sing:
  For we, which now behold these present days,
  Have eyes to wonder, but lack tongues to praise.

        — *William Shakespeare*

On Nights Like This
All Cities Are Alike

On nights like this all cities are alike,
with cloud-flags hung.
The banners by the storm are flung,
torn out like hair
in any country anywhere
whose boundaries and rivers are uncertain.
In every garden is a pond,
the same little house sits just beyond;
the same light is in all the houses;
and all the people look alike
and hold their hands before their faces.

On nights like this my little sister grows,
who was born and died before me, very small.
There have been many such nights, gone long ago:
she must be lovely now. Soon the suitors will call.

— *Rainer Maria Rilke*
TRANSLATED BY C. F. MACINTYRE

On the Death of Ianthe

Well I remember how you smiled
    To see me write your name upon
The soft sea-sand . . . *"O! what a child!*
    You think you're writing upon stone!"
I have since written what no tide
    Shall ever wash away, what men
Unborn shall read o'er ocean wide
    And find Ianthe's name agen.

         — Walter Savage Landor

Song

FROM TWELFTH NIGHT, ACT II, SCENE III

O mistress mine, where are you roaming?
O, stay and hear; your true love's coming,
    That can sing both high and low:
Trip no further, pretty sweeting;
Journeys end in lovers' meeting,
    Every wise man's son doth know.

What is love? 'tis not hereafter;
Present mirth hath present laughter;
    What's to come is still unsure:
In delay there lies no plenty;
Then come and kiss me, sweet and twenty,
    Youth's a stuff will not endure.

— *William Shakespeare*

The Muse

When in the night I await her coming
My life seems stopped. I ask myself: What
Are tributes, freedom, or youth compared
To this treasured friend holding a flute?
Look, she's coming! She drops her veil
And watches me, steady and long. I say:
"Was it you who dictated to Dante the pages
Of Hell?" and she answers: "I am the one."

— *Anna Akhmatova*
TRANSLATED BY STANLEY BURNSHAW

A Face

If one could have that little head or hers
    Painted upon a background of pale gold,
Such as the Tuscan's early art prefers!
    No shade encroaching on the matchless mould
Of those two lips, which should be opening soft
    In the pure profile; not as when she laughs,
For that spoils all: but rather as if aloft
    Yon hyacinth, she loves so, leaned its staff's
Burthen of honey-coloured buds to kiss
And capture 'twixt the lips apart for this.
Then her lithe neck, three fingers might surround,
How it should waver on the pale gold ground
Up to the fruit-shaped, perfect chin it lifts!
I know, Correggio loves to mass, in rifts
Of heaven, his angel faces, orb on orb
Breaking its outline, burning shades absorb:
But these are only massed there, I should think,
    Waiting to see some wonder momently
    Grow out, stand full, fade slow against the sky
    (That's the pale ground you'd see this sweet face by),
    All heaven, meanwhile, condensed into one eye
Which fears to lose the wonder, should it wink.

– Robert Browning

85

To a Fair Lady, Playing with a Snake

Strange! that such Horror and such Grace
Should dwell together in one place;
A Furie's Arm, an Angel's Face.

'Tis innocence, and youth, which makes
In *Chloris'* fancy such mistakes,
To start at Love, and play with Snakes.

By this and by her coldness barr'd,
Her servants have a task too hard;
The Tyrant has a double guard!

Thrice happy Snake! that in her sleeve
May boldly creep, we dare not give
Our thoughts so unconfin'd a leave.

Contented in that nest of Snow
He lies, as he his bliss did know,
And to the wood no more would go.

Take heed, fair *Eve!* you do not make
Another Tempter of this Snake;
A marble one so warmed would speak.

— *Edmund Waller*

Vittoria Colonna

Once more, once more, Inarimé,
    I see thy purple halls!—once more
I hear the billows of the bay
    Wash the white pebbles on thy shore.

High o'er the sea-surge and the sands,
    Like a great galleon wrecked and cast
Ashore by storms, thy castle stands,
    A mouldering landmark of the Past.

Upon its terrace-walk I see
    A phantom gliding to and fro;
It is Colonna,—it is she
    Who lived and loved so long ago.

Pescara's beautiful young wife,
    The type of perfect womanhood,
Whose life was love, the life of life,
    That time and change and death withstood.

For death, that breaks the marriage band
    In others, only closer pressed
The wedding-ring upon her hand
    And closer locked and barred her breast.

She knew the life-long martyrdom,
    The weariness, the endless pain
Of waiting for some one to come
    Who nevermore would come again.

The shadows of the chestnut trees,
    The odor of the orange blooms,
The song of birds, and more than these,
    The silence of deserted rooms;

The respiration of the sea,
    The soft caresses of the air,
All things in nature seemed to be
    But ministers of her despair;

Till the o'erburdened heart, so long
    Imprisoned in itself, found vent
And voice in one impassioned song
    Of inconsolable lament.

Then as the sun, though hidden from sight,
    Transmutes to gold the leaden mist,
Her life was interfused with light,
    From realms that, though unseen, exist.

Inarimé! Inarimé!
    Thy castle on the crags above
In dust shall crumble and decay,
    But not the memory of her love.

– Henry Wadsworth Longfellow

Leofric and Godiva

In every hour, in every mood,
O lady, it is sweet and good
To bathe the soul in prayer,
And at the close of such a day,
When we have ceased to bless and pray,
To dream on thy long hair.

— *Walter Savage Landor*

Deirdre

Do not let any woman read this verse;
It is for men, and after them their sons
And their son's sons.

The time comes when our hearts sink utterly;
When we remember Deirdre and her tale,
And that her lips are dust.

Once she did tread the earth: men took her hand;
They looked into her eyes and said their say,
And she replied to them.

More than a thousand years it is since she
Was beautiful: she trod the grass;
She saw the clouds.

A thousand years! The grass is still the same,
The clouds as lovely as they were that time
When Deirdre was alive.

But there has never been a woman born
Who was so beautiful, not one so beautiful
Of all the women born.

Let all men go apart and mourn together;
No man can love her; not a man
Can ever be her lover.

No man can bend before her: no man say—
What could one say to her? There are no words
That one could say to her!

Now she is but a story that is told
beside the fire! No man can ever be
The friend of that poor queen.

— *James Stephens*

Daphne

Roots spring from my feet, Apollo, like a tree
The silver laurels grow deep into me.
Undone, undone, these thoughts of mine that beat
With a great vigor in the drouth and heat,
So my blood answers, so with sap my veins,
So as a leaf in whom no wind complains.
This is the metamorphosis, this the change
Through which my days now range:
That which was *I*, am now no longer *I*,
Among my branches let the wild birds cry,
Around me let the alien rivers flow,
Beneath my shade let other maidens go.

— *Marya Zaturenska*

Dianae Sumus in Fide

Boys and girls, we pledge allegiance
to the moon, virgin Diana,
chastity and innocence,
boys and girls all sing Diana.

O divinity, divinest
fruit of Jove, all-powerful sire,
and his Latona, your mother,
gave you birth beneath the sacred

olive tree of Delos, made you
(sing Diana) mistress of the hills,
young forests, hidden valleys
where far winding rivers
disappear in music, sing Diana.

Women in childbirth call upon your name
night goddess, queen of darkness
and false daylight. Sing Diana

who has steered the circling voyage
of the seasons into years,
bringing with her harvest time
and full granaries and rich farms:

by whatever name we call you,
(sing Diana) hear our prayers,
as years long gone you sheltered us
your sons of Romulus from harm
defend, now and forever, sing Diana!

— *Catullus*

TRANSLATED BY HORACE GREGORY

Hymn to Venus

Darling of Gods and Men, beneath the gliding stars
you fill rich earth and buoyant sea with your presence
for every living thing achieves its life through you,
rises and sees the sun. For you the sky is clear,
the tempests still. Deft earth scatters her gentle flowers,
the level ocean laughs, the softened heavens glow
with generous light for you. In the first days of spring
when the untrammelled allrenewing southwind blows
the birds exult in you and herald your coming.
Then the shy cattle leap and swim the brooks for love.
Everywhere, through all seas mountains and waterfalls,
love caresses all hearts and kindles all creatures
to overmastering lust and ordained renewals.
Therefore, since you alone control the sum of things
and nothing without you comes forth into the light
and nothing beautiful or glorious can be
without you, Alma Venus! trim my poetry
with your grace; and give peace to write and read and
     think.

                                        – *Lucretius*
                        TRANSLATED BY BASIL BUNTING

Santorin

(A Legend of the Aegean)

"Who are you, Sea Lady,
And where in the seas are we?
I have too long been steering
By the flashes in your eyes.
Why drops the moonlight through my heart,
And why so quietly
Go the great engines of my boat
As if their souls were free?"
"Oh ask me not, bold sailor;
Is not your ship a magic ship
That sails without a sail:
Are not these isles the Isles of Greece
And dust upon the sea?
But answer me three questions
And give me answers three.
What is your ship?" "A British."
"And where may Britain be?"
"Oh it lies north, dear lady;
It is a small country."
"Yet you will know my lover,
Though you live far away:
And you will whisper where he has gone,

That lily boy to look upon
And whiter than the spray."
"How should I know your lover,
Lady of the sea?"
"Alexander, Alexander,
The King of the World was he."
"Weep not for him, dear lady,
But come aboard my ship.
So many years ago he died,
He's dead as dead can be."
"O base and brutal sailor
To tell this lie to me.
His mother was the foam-foot
Star-sparkling Aphrodite;
His father was Adonis
Who lives away in Lebanon,
In stony Lebanon, where blooms
His red anemone.
But where is Alexander,
The soldier Alexander,
My golden love of olden days
The King of the World and me?"

She sank into the moonlight
And the sea was only sea.

– *James Elroy Flecker*

Birthright

Lord Rameses of Egypt sighed
Because a summer evening passed;
And little Ariadne cried
That summer fancy fell at last
To dust; and young Verona died
When beauty's hour was overcast.

Theirs was the bitterness we know
Because the clouds of hawthorn keep
So short a state, and kisses go
To tombs unfathomably deep,
While Rameses and Romeo
And little Ariadne sleep.

— John Drinkwater

A Pair of Sea-Green Eyes

Kate's eyes were sea-green. She was one of the last
    To have them that hue
    Though in the distant past
It was common enough, that's true.
    Sea-green! What's that you say?
    Impossible? A lie?
No. It's no mistake. They weren't just grey,
    But the *oculi caesii*
    Tacitus refers to,
The "eagle hath not so green,
    So quick, so fair, an eye"
Of Shakespeare—Plautus's *oculi herbei,*
And the great eyes with a green circle
    Bacon thought promised long life.
    Have you not even read Villa Real's
    Great treatise in praise of green eyes?
Then you know nothing whatever about them,
Yet you tell a man like me that he lies!
Enough! You are like the carpenter in Chaucer's tale
"Who knew not Catoun," or those who thought,
In Dryden's lines, they had somehow got
By intuition more about the Godhead to know
Than Aristotle found by reason, or Plato,
Or Plutarch, or Seneca, or Cicero.

             – *Hugh MacDiarmid*

Gone

Where's the Queen of Sheba?
Where King Solomon?
Gone with Boy Blue who looks after the sheep,
Gone and gone and gone.

Lovely is the sunshine;
Lovely is the wheat;
Lovely the wind from out of the clouds
Having its way with it.

Rise up, Old Green-Stalks!
Delve deep, Old Corn!
But where's the Queen of Sheba?
Where King Solomon?

– Walter de la Mare

SECTION V

We Were the Heroes

Voices of Heroes

OVERHEARD IN A CHURCHYARD DEDICATED
TO THE MEMORY OF 1776

"The cemetery stone New England autumn
Restores health to our voices,
Even our faces
Seem to reappear through gliding mist that gathers
In an unshuttered, moonlit, empty room.
We were the heroes, O wives, mothers, daughters!
Of war that lighted fires
Within these shores.

Upon our graves: you will find nothing there
unlike our common clay
That blows away,
Or mixed with water serves to build a wall;
But you might well imagine
That earth and air
Are relics of the True, Original Cross,
And that the trampled grass
Holds the imprint of Adam's image on this small hill—
Or you might say,
'Because Their bones lie here,
The bleak earth glows with sunlight from their eyes;
These are the heroes
And their voices speak among us at their will.'

104

Yet too much praise leaves much unsaid:
Even in death we were, somehow, more human,
Moving among the shades of things we loved or hated,
Clasping the shadows of pretty girls, of restless women,
Or quarreling with a landlord,
Or gazing with regret at empty bottles,
Or shouldering old rifles,
Or for an hundred years (since we were freed from labor)
Playing at cards with a distrusted neighbor.
It is not true that we were always sad,
Or like evil, unquiet dead misspent our fury
Among cries of death at night in winter storms—
But the earthly spirit that fed our hearts had gone,
Gone with the hope of richer farms,
Or brighter towns, or countless money;
We had learned that there were no stakes to be won,
That the unnamed, vital essence returned to God.

Now that another war flames in the east
(We can see its fires reflected in the sky
And there are more than rumors in the air)
Remember that we died fighting for what you are—
better to die
Than to sit watching the world die,
Better to sleep and learn at last
That terror and loss
Have not utterly destroyed us,
That even our naked shades

Still looked and talked like men—
That when we wake,
A little courage has earned our right to speak.

Remember that old wars remain unfinished,
That men fail, fall and are replenished
As grass grows over earth, our names forgotten,
Or misread, misspelled in ivy-covered stone
With wreaths above our graves in summer's green—
Is that blaze the blaze of lightning from a cloud?
Is that noise the coming of October rain?
We do not fear them; we know that flesh is mortal
And in a world at war, only the wars live on."

– *Horace Gregory*

Song

The glories of our blood and state
　Are shadows, not substantial things;
There is no armour against fate;
　Death lays his icy hand on kings:
　　Sceptre and crown
　　Must tumble down,
And in the dust be equal made
With the poor crooked scythe and spade.

Some men with swords may reap the field,
　And plant fresh laurels where they kill;
But their strong nerves at last must yield;
　They tame but one another still:
　　Early or late,
　　They stoop to fate,
And must give up their murmuring breath,
When they, pale captives, creep to death.

The garlands wither on your brow,
　Then boast no more your mighty deeds;
Upon Death's purple altar now,
　See, where the victor-victim bleeds:

Your heads must come
To the cold tomb,
Only the actions of the just
Smell sweet, and blossom in their dust.

– *James Shirley*

Alexandrian Kings

The Alexandrians came in a crowd
To see the children of Cleopatra,
Kaisarion, and Kaisarion's little brothers,
Alexander and Ptolemy, who for the first
Time were being taken to the Sports Ground
In a wonderful military parade.

Alexander—him they called King of
Armenia, and of Media, and of the Parthians,
Ptolemy—they called him King
Of Kilikia, of Syria, and of Phoinikê.
Kaisarion was standing a little forward,
Dressed in pink tinted silk,
On his breast a garland of hyacinths,
His belt a double row of sapphires and amethysts;
His shoes were tied with white ribbons
Embroidered with rosy-coloured pearls.
They called him rather more than the little ones,
Him they called King of Kings.

The Alexandrians understood of course
That this was only words and play acting.

But the day was poetical and warm,
The sky blue, a pale blue,

And the Alexandrian Sports Ground a
Triumph of artistic achievement;
The magnificence of the courtiers extraordinary,
Kaisarion all grace and beauty
 (Cleopatra's son, blood of the children of Lagos);
The Alexandrians flocked to the festival,
And were enthusiastic, and began to applaud,
In Greek, in Egyptian, and some in Hebrew,
Enchanted with the lovely spectacle—
Although they knew of course what it was worth,
What empty words these Kingships.

– *C. P. Cavafy*
TRANSLATED BY JOHN MAVROGORDATO

The Silent Slain

We too, we too, descending once again
The hills of our own land, we too have heard
Far off—Ah, que ce cor a longue haleine—
The horn of Roland in the passages of Spain,
The first, the second blast, the failing third,
And with the third turned back and climbed once more
The steep road southward, and heard faint the sound
Of swords, of horses, the disastrous war,
And crossed the dark defile at last, and found
At Roncevaux upon the darkening plain
The dead against the dead and on the silent ground
The silent slain—

– Archibald MacLeish

Choruses from "The Rock"

VIII

There came one who spoke of the shame of Jerusalem
And the holy places defiled;
Peter the Hermit, scourging with words.
And among his hearers were a few good men,
Many who were evil,
And most who were neither.
Like all men in all places,

Some went from love of glory,
Some went who were restless and curious,
Some were rapacious and lustful.
Many left their bodies to the kites of Syria
Or sea-strewn along the routes;
Many left their souls in Syria,
Living on, sunk in moral corruption;
Many came back well broken,
Diseased and beggared, finding
A stranger at the door in possession:
Came home cracked by the sun of the East
And the seven deadly sins in Syria.

But our King did well at Acre.
And in spite of all the dishonour,

The broken standards, the broken lives,
The broken faith in one place or another,
There was something left that was more than the tales
Of old men on winter evenings.
Only the faith could have done what was good of it,
Whole faith of a few,
Part faith of many.
Not avarice, lechery, treachery,
Envy, sloth, gluttony, jealousy, pride:
It was not these that made the Crusades,
But these that unmade them.

Remember the faith that took men from home
At the call of a wandering preacher.
Our age is an age of moderate virtue
And of moderate vice
When men will not lay down the Cross
Because they will never assume it.
Yet nothing is impossible, nothing,
To men of faith and conviction.
Let us therefore make perfect our will.
O GOD, help us.

— *T. S. Eliot*

The Chase

In search through gardens, woods,
in sedan, on horse, or foot,
the bird, the goose, the hare,
the jewel in the fish,
the nymph that lingers where
moss and water at the blare
of trumpets, horns, like dreamy
musings disappear, the nymph,
the goose, the bird, the hare
are nothing but excuse
for chasing what is glorious
in all, and everywhere.

From *that* to *this,* and not
the process turned about;
why else would hunters bleed,
and the hunted sing aloud?

— *Arthur Gregor*

Robin Hood

TO A FRIEND

No! THOSE days are gone away,
And their hours are old and gray,
And their minutes buried all
Under the down-trodden pall
Of the leaves of many years:
Many times have winter's shears,
Frozen North, and chilling East,
Sounded tempests to the feast
Of the forest's whispering fleeces,
Since men knew nor rent nor leases.

No, the bugle sounds no more,
And the twanging bow no more;
Silent is the ivory shrill
Past the heath and up the hill;
There is no mid-forest laugh,
Where lone Echo gives the half
To some wight, amaz'd to hear
Jesting, deep in forest drear.

On the fairest time of June
You may go, with sun or moon,

Or the seven stars to light you,
Or the polar ray to right you;
But you never may behold
Little John, or Robin bold;
Never one, of all the clan,
Thrumming on an empty can
Some old hunting ditty, while
He doth his green way beguile
To fair hostess Merriment,
Down beside the pasture Trent;
For he left the merry tale
Messenger for spicy ale.

Gone, the merry morris din;
Gone, the song of Gamelyn;
Gone, the tough-belted outlaw
Idling in the "grenè shawe";
All are gone away and past!
And if Robin should be cast
Sudden from his turfed grave,
And if Marian should have
Once again her forest days,
She would weep, and he would craze:
He would swear, for all his oaks,
Fall'n beneath the dockyard strokes,
Have rotted on the briny seas;
She would weep that her wild bees

Sang not to her—strange! that honey
Can't be got without hard money!

So it is: yet let us sing,
Honour to the old bow-string!
Honour to the bugle-horn!
Honour to the woods unshorn!
Honour to the Lincoln green!
Honour to the archer keen!
Honour to tight Little John,
And the horse he rode upon!
Honour to bold Robin Hood,
Sleeping in the underwood!
Honour to Maid Marian,
And to all the Sherwood-clan!
Though their days have hurried by
Let us two a burden try.

– *John Keats*

The Sweetness of Nature

Endlessly over the water
    Birds of the Bann are singing;
Sweeter to me their voices
    Than any churchbell's ringing.

Over the plain of Moyra
    Under the heels of foemen,
I saw my people broken
    As flax is scutched by women.

But the cries I hear by Derry
    Are not of men triumphant;
I hear their calls in the evening,
    Swans calm and exultant.

I hear the stag's belling
    Over the valley's steepness;
No music in the earth
    Can move me like its sweetness.

Christ, Christ hear me!
    Christ, Christ of Thy meekness!
Christ, Christ love me!
    Sever me not from Thy sweetness!

– Anonymous

TRANSLATED FROM THE IRISH BY

FRANK O'CONNOR

We Be Soldiers Three

We be soldiers three,
Pardonnez-moi je vous en prie,
Lately come forth of the low country,
With never a penny of money.
Here, good fellow, I drink to thee,
Pardonnez-moi je vous en prie,
To all good fellows wherever they be,
With never a penny of money.
And he that will not pledge me this,
Pardonnez-moi je vous en prie,
Pays for the shot, whatever it is,
With never a penny of money.
Charge it again, boys charge it again,
Pardonnez-moi je vous en prie,
As long as you have any ink in your pen,
With never a penny of money.

– *Anonymous*

His Cavalier

Give me that man, that dares bestride
The active Sea-horse, & with pride,
Through that huge field of waters ride:
Who, with his looks too, can appease
The ruffling winds and raging Seas,
In mid'st of all their outrages.
This, this a virtuous man can doe,
Saile against Rocks, and split them too;
I! and a world of Pikes passe through.

– Robert Herrick

The Silver Tassie

Go, fetch to me a pint o' wine,
    An' fill it in a silver tassie;
That I may drink, before I go,
    A service to my bonnie lassie.
The boat rocks at the pier o' Leith,
    Fu' loud the wind blaws frae the ferry,
The ship rides by the Berwick-law,
    And I maun leave my bonnie Mary.

The trumpets sound, the banners fly,
    The glittering spears are rankèd ready;
The shouts o' war are heard afar,
    The battle closes thick and bloody;
But it's no the roar o' sea or shore
    Wad mak me langer wish to tarry;
Nor shout o' war that's heard afar,
    It's leaving thee, my bonnie Mary.

– Robert Burns

Burial of the Minnisink

On sunny slope and beechen swell
The shadowed light of evening fell;
And, where the maple's leaf was brown,
With soft and silent lapse came down,
The glory, that the wood receives,
At sunset, in its golden leaves.

Far upward in the mellow light
Rose the blue hills. One cloud of white,
Around a far uplifted cone,
In the warm blush of evening shone;
An image of the silver lakes,
By which the Indian's soul awakes.

But soon a funeral hymn was heard
Where the soft breath of evening stirred
The tall, gray forest; and a band
Of stern in heart, and strong in hand,
Came winding down beside the wave,
To lay the red chief in his grave.

They sang, that by his native bowers
He stood, in the last moon of flowers,
And thirty snows had not yet shed
Their glory on the warrior's head;
But, as the summer fruit decays,
So died he in those naked days.

A dark cloud of the roebuck's skin
Covered the warrior, and within
Its heavy folds the weapons, made
For the hard toils of war, were laid;
The cuirass, woven of plaited reeds,
And the broad belt of shells and beads.

Before, a dark-haired virgin train
Chanted the death dirge of the slain;
Behind, the long procession came
Of hoary men and chiefs of fame,
With heavy hearts, and eyes of grief,
Leading the war-horse of their chief.

Stripped of his proud and martial dress,
Uncurbed, unreined, and riderless,
With darting eye, and nostril spread,
And heavy and impatient tread,
He came; and oft that eye so proud
Asked for his rider in the crowd.

They buried the dark chief; they freed
Beside the grave his battle steed;
And swift an arrow cleaved its way
To his stern heart! One piercing neigh
Arose, and, on the dead man's plain,
The rider grasps his steed again.

– *Henry Wadsworth Longfellow*

The Returned Volunteer
to his Rifle

Over this hearth—my father's seat—
　　Repose, to patriot-memory dear,
Thou tried companion, whom at last I greet
　　By steepy banks of Hudson here.
How oft I told thee of this scene—
The Highlands blue—the river's narrowing sheen.
Little at Gettysburg we thought
To find such haven; but God kept it green.
Long rest! with belt, and bayonet, and canteen.

– *Herman Melville*

My Fathers Came from Kentucky

I was born in Illinois,—
Have lived there many days.
And I have Northern words,
And thoughts,
And ways.

But my great-grandfathers came
To the west with Daniel Boone,
And taught his babes to read,
And heard the red-bird's tune;

And heard the turkey's call,
And stilled the panther's cry,
And rolled on the blue-grass hills,
And looked God in the eye.

And feud and Hell were theirs;
Love, like the moon's desire,
Love like a burning-mine,
Love like rifle-fire.

I tell tales out of school
Till these Yankees hate my style.
Why should the young cad cry,
Shout with joy for a mile?

Why do I faint with love
Till the prairies dip and reel?
My heart is a kicking horse
Shod with Kentucky steel.

No drop of my blood from north
Of Mason and Dixon's line.
And this racer in my breast
Tears my ribs for a sign.

But I ran in Kentucky hills
Last week. They were hearth and home. . . .
And the church at Grassy Springs,
Under the red-bird's wings
Was peace and honeycomb.

– Vachel Lindsay

Crossing the Plains

What great yoked brutes with briskets low,
With wrinkled necks like buffalo,
With round, brown, liquid, pleading eyes,
That turn'd so low and sad to you,
That shone like love's eyes soft with tears,
That seemed to plead and make replies,
And while they bow'd their necks and drew
The creaking load: and look'd at you.
Their sable briskets swept the ground,
Their cloven feet kept solemn sound.

Two sullen bullocks led the line,
Their great eyes shining bright like wine;
Two sullen captive kings were they,
That had in time held herds at bay,
And even now they crushed the sod
With stolid sense of majesty,
And stately stepp'd and stately trod,
As if 'twere something still to be
Kings even in captivity.

— Joaquin Miller

Buffalo Bill's
Defunct

Buffalo Bill's
defunct
        who used to
        ride a watersmooth-silver
                                stallion
and break onetwothreefourfive pigeonsjustlikethat
                                        Jesus

he was a handsome man
                        and what i want to know is
how do you like your blueeyed boy
Mister Death

                                    — *E. E. Cummings*

An Irish Airman Foresees his Death

FOR MAJOR ROBERT GREGORY

I know that I shall meet my fate
Somewhere among the clouds above;
Those that I fight I do not hate,
Those that I guard I do not love;
My country is Kiltartan Cross,
My countrymen Kiltartan's poor,
No likely end could bring them loss
Or leave them happier than before.
Nor law, nor duty bade me fight,
Nor public men, nor cheering crowds,
A lonely impulse of delight
Drove to this tumult in the clouds;
I balanced all, brought all to mind,
The years to come seemed waste of breath,
A waste of breath the years behind
In balance with this life, this death.

– *William Butler Yeats*

Bewick Finzer

Time was when his half million drew
    The breath of six per cent;
But soon the worm of what-was-not
    Fed hard on his content;
And something crumbled in his brain
    When his half million went.

Time passed, and filled along with his
    The place of many more;
Time came, and hardly one of us
    Had credence to restore,
From what appeared one day, the man
    Whom we had known before.

The broken voice, the withered neck,
    The coat worn out with care,
The cleanliness of indigence,
    The brilliance of despair,
The fond imponderable dreams
    Of affluence,—all were there.

Poor Finzer, with his dreams and schemes,
    Fares hard now in the race,
With heart and eye that have a task

When he looks in the face
Of one who might so easily
    Have been in Finzer's place.

He comes unfailing for the loan
    We give and then forget;
He comes, and probably for years
    Will he be coming yet,—
Familiar as an old mistake,
    And futile as regret.

– Edwin Arlington Robinson

Song: Lift-Boy

Let me tell you the story of how I began:
I began as the knife-boy and ended as the boot-man,
With nothing in my pockets but a jack-knife and a button,
With nothing in my pockets but a jack-knife and a button,
With nothing in my pockets.

Let me tell you the story of how I went on:
I began as the lift-boy and ended as the lift-man,
With nothing in my pockets but a jack-knife and a button,
With nothing in my pockets but a jack-knife and a button,
With nothing in my pockets.

I found it very easy to whistle and play
With nothing in my head or my pockets all day,
With nothing in my pockets.

But along came Old Eagle, like Moses or David,
He stopped at the fourth floor and preached me Damnation:
'Not a soul shall be savèd, not one shall be savèd.
The whole First Creation shall forfeit salvation:
From knife-boy to lift-boy, from ragged to regal,
Not one shall be savèd, not you, not Old Eagle,
No soul on earth escapeth, even if all repent——'
So I cut the cords of the lift and down we went,
With nothing in our pockets.

– Robert Graves

SECTION VI

How Many Heavens . . .

How Many Heavens . . .

The emeralds are singing on the grasses,
And in the trees the bells of the long cold are ringing—
My blood seems changed to emeralds like the spears
Of grass beneath the earth piercing and singing.

The flame of the first blade
Is an angel piercing through the earth to sing
'God is everything!
The grass within the grass, the angel in the angel, flame
Within the flame, and He is the green shade that came
To be the heart of shade.'

The grey-beard angel of the stone,
Who has grown wise with age, cried 'Not alone
Am I within my silence—God is the stone in the still stone,
    the silence laid
In the heart of silence' . . . then, above the glade,

The yellow straws of light,
Whereof the sun has built his nest, cry 'Bright
Is the world, the yellow straw
My brother—God is the straw within the straw:—All
    things are Light.'

He is the sea of ripeness and the sweet apple's emerald lore.
So you, my flame of grass, my root of the world from which
   all Spring shall grow,
O you, my hawthorn bough of the stars, now leaning low
Through the day, for your flowers to kiss my lips, shall
   know
He is the core of the heart of love, and He, beyond laboring
   seas, our ultimate shore.

– Dame Edith Sitwell

Peace

My soul, there is a country
    Far beyond the stars,
Where stands a wingèd sentry
    All skilful in the wars:
There, above noise and danger,
    Sweet Peace sits crowned with smiles,
And One born in a manger
    Commands the beauteous files.
He is thy gracious Friend,
    And—O my soul, awake!—
Did in pure love descend
    To die here for thy sake.
If thou canst get but thither,
    There grows the flower of Peace,
The Rose that cannot wither,
    Thy fortress, and thy ease.
Leave then thy foolish ranges;
    For none can thee secure
But One who never changes—
    Thy God, thy Life, thy Cure.

– Henry Vaughan

Variation on a Polish Folk Song

Joy! Joy! Joy! that on my quiet day
In the dull house where never a sound
Echoed and entered, where I sat forever waiting,
The long, gray shadow crossed my way;
I saw the renowned grayhound
Speeding across dry fields, across my floor,
So clean, sand-sprinkled, poor.

An ardent beast, half-tamed, hesitating,
I thought him till his eyes shot flame;
They seemed to call me to the illimitable lands,
Into the very far,
Till I forgot my world, my life, my name.
And then I heard the unearthly wail of a horn
Sound from the world of the unborn,
And a red-ringed falling star.

And galloping across my field on a black horse,
A lone, fiery Hussar,
Who smiled and looked at me
While the great grayhound licked my hands.
Gently he waits, his mute eyes speak to me
(Unintelligible and irresistible the call!)
Of the great, patient animal

Who spoke in the Hussar's eyes,
Who drove his madman's course,
Flies skyward with my soul on his black horse
Toward some great, groaning sea,
Who sends his grayhound emissary!

Day after day I lie and talk to him,
Helpless on my sick-bed,
In the mute language of the seraphim,
And by unbearable longing led
My closing eyes are humbly questioning.
Tell me, O lean, fierce creature, gently bred
Of your Master, the Lord of the Dead,
Who brings such learning to the poor unread,
Whom the falling constellations bring,
And the tempest's whirling wing,
Who takes the Hussar's form,
And rides in angry beauty through the storm!

– *Marya Zaturenska*

Heaven

O who will show me those delights on high?
> *Echo.   I.*

Thou Echo, thou art mortall, all men know.
> *Echo.   No.*

Wert thou not born among the trees and leaves?
> *Echo.   Leaves.*

And are there any leaves that still abide?
> *Echo.   Bide.*

What leaves are they? Impart the matter wholly.
> *Echo.   Holy.*

Are holy leaves the Echo then of blisse?
> *Echo.   Yes.*

Then tell me, what is that supreme delight?
> *Echo.   Light.*

Light to the minde; what shall the will enjoy?
> *Echo.   Joy.*

But are there cares and businesse with the pleasure?
> *Echo.   Leisure.*

Light, joy, and leisure; but shall they persever?
> *Echo.   Ever.*

– George Herbert

For a Picture of St. Dorothea

I bear a basket lined with grass;
I am so light, I am so fair,
That men must wonder as I pass
And at the basket that I bear,
There in a newly-drawn green litter
Sweet flowers I carry,—sweets for bitter.

Lilies I shew you, lilies none,
None in Caesar's gardens blow,—
And a quince in hand,—not one
Is set upon your boughs below;
Not set, because their buds not spring;
Spring not, 'cause world is wintering.

But these were found in the East and South
Where Winter is the clime forgot.—
The dewdrop on the larkspur's mouth
O should it then be quenchèd not?
In starry water-meads they drew
These drops: which be they? stars or dew?

Had she a quince in hand? Yet gaze:
Rather it is the sizing moon.
Lo, linkèd heavens with milky ways!

That was her larkspur row.—So soon?
Sphered so fast, sweet soul?—We see
Nor fruits, nor flowers, nor Dorothy.

— *Gerard Manly Hopkins*

The Animals

They do not live in the world,
Are not in time and space,
From birth to death hurled
No word do they have, not one
To plant a foot upon,
Were never in any place.

For by words the world was called
Out of the empty air,
With words was shaped and walled—
Line and circle and square,
Dust and emerald,—
Snatched from deceiving death
By the articulate breath.

But these have never trod
Twice the familiar track,
Never never turned back
Into the memoried day;
All is new and near
In the unchanging Here
Of the fifth great day of God,

That shall remain the same,
Never shall pass away.

On the sixth day we came.

– Edwin Muir

The Viper

Barefoot I went and made no sound;
The earth was hot beneath:
The air was quivering around,
The circling kestrel eyed the ground
And hung above the heath.

There in the pathway stretched along
The lovely serpent lay:
She reared not up the heath among,
She bowed her head, she sheathed her tongue,
And shining stole away.

Fair was the brave embroidered dress,
Fairer the gold eyes shone:
Loving her not, yet I did bless
The fallen angel's comeliness;
And gazed when she had gone.

— *Ruth Pitter*

Who Is That
A-Walking in the Corn

Who is that a-walking in the corn?
I have looked to East and looked to West
But nowhere could I find Him who walks
    Master's cornfield in the morning.

Who is that a-walking in the corn?
Is it Joshua, the son of Nun?—
Or King David come to fight the giant
    Near the cornfield in the morning?

Who is that a-walking in the corn?
Is it Peter jangling Heaven's keys?—
Or old Gabriel come to blow his horn
    Near the cornfield in the morning?

Who is that a-walking in the corn?
I have looked to East and looked to West
But nowhere could I find Him who walks
    Master's cornfield in the morning.

– Fenton Johnson

SECTION VII

I Saw a Peacock with a Fiery Tail

I Saw a Peacock

I saw a peacock with a fiery tail
I saw a blazing comet drop down hail
I saw a cloud wrapped with ivy round
I saw an oak creep on along the ground
I saw a pismire swallow up a whale
I saw the sea brim full of ale
I saw a Venice glass full fathom deep
I saw a well full of men's tears that weep
I saw red eyes all of a flaming fire
I saw a house bigger than the moon and higher
I saw the sun at twelve o'clock at night
I saw the man that saw this wondrous sight.

— *Anonymous*

Kalamazoo

Once, in the city of Kalamazoo,
The gods went walking, two and two,
With the friendly phoenix, the stars of Orion,
The speaking pony and singing lion.
For in Kalamazoo in a cottage apart
Lived the girl with the innocent heart.

Thenceforth the city of Kalamazoo
Was the envied, intimate chum of the sun.
He rose from a cave by the principal street.
The lions sang, the dawn-horn blew,
And the ponies danced on silver feet.
He hurled his clouds of love around;
Deathless colors of his old heart
Draped the houses and dyed the ground.
Oh shrine of the wide young Yankee land,
Incense city of Kalamazoo,
That held, in the midnight, the priceless sun
As a jeweller holds an opal in his hand!

From the awkward city of Oshkosh came
Love the bully no whip shall tame,
Bringing his gang of sinners bold.
And I was the least of his Oshkosh men;

But none were reticent, none were old.
And we joined the singing phoenix then,
And shook the lilies of Kalamazoo
All for one hidden butterfly.
Bulls of glory, in cars of war
We charged the boulevards, proud to die
For her ribbon sailing there on high.
Our blood set gutters all aflame,
Where the sun slept without any shame,
Cold rock till he must rise again.
She made great poets of wolf-eyed men—
The dear queen-bee of Kalamazoo,
With her crystal wings, and her honey heart.
We fought for her favors a year and a day
(Oh, the bones of the dead, the Oshkosh dead,
That were scattered along her pathway red!)
And then, in her harum-scarum way,
She left with a passing traveller-man—
With a singing Irishman
Went to Japan.

Why do the lean hyenas glare
Where the glory of Artemis had begun—
Of Atalanta, Joan of Arc,
Lorna Doone, Rosy O'Grady,
And Orphant Annie all in one?
Who burned this city of Kalamazoo

Till nothing was left but a ribbon or two—
One scorched phoenix that mourned in the dew,
Acres of ashes, a junk-man's cart,
A torn-up letter, a dancing shoe
(And the bones of the valiant dead)?
Who burned this city of Kalamazoo—
Love-town, Troy-town Kalamazoo?

A harum-scarum innocent heart.

— Vachel Lindsay

Sarah Byng

WHO COULD NOT READ AND WAS TOSSED

INTO A THORNY HEDGE BY A BULL

Some years ago you heard me sing
My doubts on Alexander Byng.
His sister Sarah now inspires
My jaded Muse, my failing fires.
Of Sarah Byng the tale is told
How when the child was twelve years old
She could not read or write a line.

Her sister Jane, though barely nine,
Could spout the Catechism through
And parts of Matthew Arnold too,
While little Bill
          who came between
Was quite unnaturally keen
        On
         'Athalie', by Jean Racine

But not so Sarah! Not so Sal!
She was a most uncultured girl

Who didn't care a pinch of snuff
For any literary stuff
And gave the classics all a miss.
Observe the consequence of this!
As she was walking home one day,
Upon the fields across her way
A gate, securely padlocked, stood,
And by its side a piece of wood
On which was painted plain and full,

BEWARE THE VERY
FURIOUS BULL.

Alas! The young illiterate
Went blindly forward to her fate,
And ignorantly climbed the gate!

Now happily the Bull that day
Was rather in the mood for play
Than goring people through and through

As Bulls so very often do;
He tossed her lightly with his horns
Into a prickly hedge of thorns,
And stood by laughing while she strode
And pushed and struggled to the road.

The lesson was not lost upon
The child, who since has always gone
A long way round to keep away
From signs, whatever they may say,
And leaves a padlocked gate alone.
Moreover she has wisely grown
Confirmed in her instinctive guess
That literature breeds distress.

— *Hillaire Belloc*

The Gardener's Song

He thought he saw an Elephant,
    That practiced on a fife:
He looked again, and found it was
    A letter from his wife.
"At length I realize," he said,
    "The bitterness of Life!"

He thought he saw a Buffalo
    Upon the chimney-piece:
He looked again, and found it was
    His Sister's Husband's Niece.
"Unless you leave this house," he said,
    "I'll send for the Police!"

He thought he saw a Rattlesnake
    That questioned him in Greek:
He looked again, and found it was
    The Middle of Next Week.
"The one thing I regret," he said,
    "Is that it cannot speak!"

He thought he saw a Banker's Clerk
    Descending from the 'bus:
He looked again, and found it was

A Hippopotamus.
"If this should stay to dine," he said,
"There won't be much for us!"

He thought he saw a Kangaroo
    That worked a coffee-mill:
He looked again, and found it was
    A Vegetable-Pill.
"Were I to swallow this," he said,
    "I should be very ill!"

He thought he saw a Coach-and-Four
    That stood beside his bed:
He looked again, and found it was
    A Bear without a Head.
"Poor thing," he said, "poor silly thing!
    It's waiting to be fed!"

He thought he saw an Albatross
    That fluttered round the lamp:

He looked again, and found it was
    A Penny-Postage-Stamp.
"You'd best be getting home," he said:
    "The nights are very damp!"

He thought he saw a Garden Door
    That opened with a key:
He looked again, and found it was
    A Double-Rule-of-Three:
"And all its mystery," he said,
    "Is clear as day to me!"

He thought he saw an Argument
    That proved he was the Pope:
He looked again, and found it was
    A bar of mottled soap.
"A fact so dread," he faintly said,
    "Extinguishes all hope!"

— *Lewis Carroll*

I Mun Be Married a Sunday

I mun be married a Sunday;
I mun be married a Sunday;
Who soever shall come that way,
I mun be married a Sunday.

Roister Doister is my name;
Roister Doister is my name;
A lusty brute I am the same;
I mun be married a Sunday.

Christian Custance have I found;
Christian Custance have I found;
A widow worth a thousand pound:
I mun be married a Sunday.

Custance is as sweet as honey;
Custance is as sweet as honey;
I her lamb, and she my coney;
I mun be married a Sunday.

When we shall make our wedding feast,
When we shall make our wedding feast,
There shall be cheer for man and beast,
I mun be married a Sunday.
      I mun be married a Sunday.

— *Nicholas Udall*

Dickey Diller and His Wife

Little Dickey Diller
Had a wife and siller;

He took a stick and broke her back,
And sent her to the miller.

The miller, with his stone dish,
Sent her unto Uncle Fish.

Uncle Fish, the good shoemaker,
Sent her unto John the baker.

John the baker, with his ten men,
Sent her unto Mistress Wren.

Mistress Wren, with grief and pain,
Sent her to the Queen of Spain.

The Queen of Spain, that woman of sin,
Opened the door and let her in.

– Anonymous

The Looking-Glass

A COUNTRY DANCE

QUEEN BESS was Harry's daughter. Stand forward
     partners all!
In ruff and stomacher and gown
She danced King Philip down-a-down,
And left her shoe to show 'twas true—
     (The very tune I'm playing you)
In Norgem at Brickwall!

The Queen was in her chamber, and she was middling
     old.
Her petticoat was satin, and her stomacher was gold.
Backwards and forwards and sideways did she pass,
Making up her mind to face the cruel looking-glass.
The cruel looking-glass that will never show a lass
As comely or as kindly or as young as what she was!

Queen Bess was Harry's daughter. Now hand your
     partners all!

The Queen was in her chamber, a-combing of her hair.
There came Queen Mary's spirit and It stood behind
     her chair,

Singing "Backwards and forwards and sideways may you pass,
But I will stand behind you till you face the looking-glass.
The cruel looking-glass that will never show a lass
As lovely or unlucky or as lonely as I was!"

Queen Bess was Harry's daughter. Now turn your partners all!

The Queen was in her chamber, a-weeping very sore,
There came Lord Leicester's spirit and It scratched upon the door,
Singing "Backwards and forwards and sideways may you pass,
But I will walk beside you till you face the looking-glass.
The cruel looking-glass that will never show a lass,
As hard or unforgiving or as wicked as you was!"

Queen Bess was Harry's daughter. Now kiss your partners all!

The Queen was in her chamber, her sins were on her head.
She looked the spirits up and down and statelily she said:—
"Backwards and forwards and sideways though I've been,
Yet I am Harry's daughter and I am England's Queen!"

And she faced the looking-glass (and whatever else there
     was)
And she saw her day was over and she saw her beauty pass
In the cruel looking-glass, that can always hurt a lass
More hard than any ghost there is or any man there was!

– Rudyard Kipling

The Falcon

I

Lully, lulley! lully, lulley!
The faucon hath born my make away!

II

He bare him up, he bare him down,
He bare him into an orchard brown.

III

In that orchard was an halle,
That was hangèd with purple and pall.

IV

And in that hall there was a bed,
It was hangèd with gold sa red.

V

And in that bed there li'th a knight,
His woundès bleeding day and night.

VI

At the bed's foot there li'th a hound,
Licking the blood as it runs down.

VII

By that bed-side kneeleth a may,
As she weepeth both night and day.

VIII

And at that bed's head standeth a stone,
Corpus Christi written thereon.

IX

Lully, lulley! lully, lulley!
The faucon hath born my make away.

— *Anonymous*

The Riddling Knight

There were three sisters fair and bright,
Jennifer, Gentle, and Rosemary,
And they three loved one valiant knight—
As the dew flies over the mulberry-tree.

The eldest sister let him in,
Jennifer, Gentle, and Rosemary,
And barr'd the door with a silver pin,
As the dew flies over the mulberry-tree.

The second sister made his bed,
Jennifer, Gentle, and Rosemary,
And placed soft pillows under his head,
As the dew flies over the mulberry-tree.

The youngest sister that same night,
Jennifer, Gentle, and Rosemary,
Was resolved for to wed wi' this valiant knight,
As the dew flies over the mulberry-tree.

'And if you can answer questions three,
Jennifer, Gentle, and Rosemary,
O then, fair maid, I'll marry wi' thee,
As the dew flies over the mulberry-tree.

'O what is louder nor a horn,
Jennifer, Gentle, and Rosemary,
O what is sharper nor a thorn?
As the dew flies over the mulberry-tree.

'Or what is heavier nor the lead,
Jennifer, Gentle, and Rosemary,
Or what is better nor the bread?
As the dew flies over the mulberry-tree.

'Or what is longer nor the way,
Jennifer, Gentle, and Rosemary,
Or what is deeper nor the sea?—'
As the dew flies over the mulberry-tree.

'O shame is louder nor a horn,
Jennifer, Gentle, and Rosemary,
And hunger is sharper nor a thorn,
As the dew flies over the mulberry-tree.

'O sin is heavier nor the lead,
Jennifer, Gentle, and Rosemary,
The blessing's better nor the bread,
As the dew flies over the mulberry-tree.

'O the wind is longer nor the way,
Jennifer, Gentle, and Rosemary,
And love is deeper nor the sea,'
As the dew flies over the mulberry-tree.

'You've answer'd my questions three.
Jennifer, Gentle, and Rosemary;
And now, fair maid, I'll marry wi' thee,'
As the dew flies over the mulberry-tree.

— Traditional: English

Melander SUPPOSED TO LOVE

Susan, BUT DID LOVE Ann

Who doth presume my Misstress's name to scan,
Goes about more then any way he can,
Since all men think that it is *Susan.* Echo *Ann.*

What say'st? Then tell who is as white as Swan,
While others set by her are pale and wan,
Then *Echo,* speak, Is it not *Susan,* Ec. *Ann.*

Tell, *Echo,* yet, whose middle's but a span,
Some being gross as bucket, round as pan;
Say, *Echo,* then, Is it not *Susan?* Ec. *Ann.*

Say, is she not soft as meal without bran,
Though yet in great haste once from me she ran,
Must I not however love *Susan?* Ec. *Ann.*

          — Edward, Lord Herbert of Cherbury

Hope

I gave to Hope a watch of mine; but he
    An anchor gave to me.
Then an old prayer-book I did present;
    And he an optick sent.
With that I gave a viall full of tears;
      But he a few green eares.
Ah Loyterer! I'le no more, no more I'le bring.
    I did expect a ring.

              – *George Herbert*

SECTION VIII

Eastward, into Sunrise

"Ya Se Van Los Pastores"

Lady, the shepherds have all gone
To Extramadura, taking their sheep with them,

Their musical instruments also, their singing:
We shall not see them again.

Therefore bring lute, flute, or other melodious
    machine,
And we shall sit under this plane-tree and perform
    upon it.

There is no help for it; use your eyes;

The shepherds, Lady, have gone into Extramadura,
Eastward, into sunrise.

                     – Dudley Fitts

Waiting for the Barbarians

What are we waiting for all crowded in the forum?
    The Barbarians are to arrive today.
Within the Senate-house why is there such inaction?
The Senators making no laws what are they sitting
        there for?
    Because the Barbarians arrive today.
    What laws now should the Senators be making?
    When the Barbarians come they'll make the laws.

Why did our Emperor get up so early in the morning?
And at the greatest city gate why is he sitting
        there now,
Upon his throne, officially, why is he wearing his
        crown?
    Because the Barbarians arrive today.
    The Emperor is waiting to receive
    Their Leader. And in fact he has prepared
    To give him an address. On it he has
    Written him down all sorts of names and titles.

Why have our two Consuls gone out, both of them,
        and the Praetors,
Today with their red togas on, with their em-
        broidered togas?

Why are they wearing bracelets, and all those
    amethysts too,
And all those rings on their fingers with splendid
    flashing emeralds?
Why should they be carrying today their precious
    walkingsticks,
With silver knobs and golden tops so wonderfully
    carved?
    Because the Barbarians will arrive today;
    Things of this sort dazzle the Barbarians.

And why are the fine orators not come here as usual
To get their speeches off, to say what they have
    to say?
    Because the Barbarians will be here today;
    And they are bored with eloquence and speech-
    making.

Why should this uneasiness begin all of a sudden,
And confusion. How serious people's faces have
    become.
Why are all the streets and squares emptying so
    quickly,
And everybody turning home again so full of thought?
    Because night has fallen and the Barbarians
    have not come.
    And some people have arrived from the frontier;
    They say there are no Barbarians any more.

And now what will become of us without Bar-
  barians?—
Those people were some sort of a solution.

– *C. P. Cavafy*
TRANSLATED BY JOHN MAVROGORDATO

The Roman Road

The Roman Road runs straight and bare
As the pale parting-line in hair
Across the heath. And thoughtful men
Contrast its days of Now and Then,
And delve, and measure, and compare;

Visioning on the vacant air
Helmed legionaries, who proudly rear
The Eagle, as they pace again
    The Roman Road.

But no tall brass-helmed legionnaire
Haunts it for me. Uprises there
A mother's form upon my ken,
Guiding my infant steps, as when
We walked that ancient thoroughfare,
    The Roman Road.

— Thomas Hardy

The Self-Unseeing

Here is the ancient floor,
Footworn and hollowed and thin,
Here was the former door
Where the dead feet walked in.

She sat here in her chair,
Smiling into the fire;
He who played stood there,
Bowing it higher and higher.

Childlike, I danced in a dream;
Blessings emblazoned that day;
Everything glowed with a gleam;
Yet we were looking away!

– *Thomas Hardy*

Fontainebleau

Interminable palaces front on the green parterres,
    And ghosts of ladies lovely and immoral
Glide down the gilded stairs,
    The high cold corridors are clicking with the heel
        taps
That long ago were theirs.

But in the sunshine, in the vague autumn sunshine,
    The geometric gardens are desolately gay;
The crimson and scarlet and rose-red dahlias
    Are painted like the ladies who used to pass this
        way
With a ringletted monarch, a Henry or a Louis
    On a lost October day.

The aisles of the garden lead into the forest,
    The aisles lead into autumn, a damp wind grieves,
Ghostly kings are hunting, the boar breaks cover,
    But the sounds of horse and horn are hushed in
        falling leaves,
    Four centuries of autumns, four centuries of leaves.

                          — *Sara Teasdale*

No Swan So Fine

'No water so still as the
     dead fountains of Versailles.' No swan,
with swart blind look askance
and gondoliering legs, so fine
     as the chintz china one with fawn-
brown eyes and toothed gold
collar on to show whose bird it was.

Lodged in the Louis Fifteenth
     candelabrum-tree of cockscomb-
tinted buttons, dahlias,
sea-urchins, and everlastings,
     it perches on the branching foam
of polished sculptured
flowers—at ease and tall. The king is dead.

— Marianne Moore

The Phoenix

SONG FROM "NEPENTHE"

O blest unfabled Incense Tree,
That burns in glorious Araby,
With red scent chalicing the air,
Till earth-life grow Elysian there!

Half buried to her flaming breast
In this bright tree, she makes her nest,
Hundred-sunned Phoenix! when she must
Crumble at length to hoary dust!

Her gorgeous death-bed! her rich pyre
Burnt up with aromatic fire!
Her urn, sight high from spoiler men!
Her birthplace when self-born again!

The mountainless green wilds among,
Here ends she her unechoing song!
With amber tears and odorous sighs
Mourned by the desert where she dies.

— *George Darley*

The Golden Palace

We go to the Golden Palace:
We set out the jade cups.
We summon the honoured guests
To enter at the Golden Gate.
They enter at the Golden Gate
And go to the Golden Hall.
In the Eastern Kitchen the meat is sliced and ready—
Roast beef and boiled pork and mutton.
The Master of the Feast hands round the wine.
The harp-players sound their clear chords.

The cups are pushed aside and we face each other
    at chess:
The rival pawns are marshalled rank against rank.
The fire glows and the smoke puffs and curls;
From the incense-burner rises a delicate fragrance.
The clear wine has made our cheeks red;
Round the table joy and peace prevail.
May those who shared in this day's delight
Through countless autumns enjoy like felicity.

– *Anonymous*
TRANSLATED BY ARTHUR WALEY

181

Lo-yang

A beautiful place is the town of Lo-yang:
The big streets are full of spring light.
The lads go driving out with harps in their hands:
The mulberry girls go out to the fields with their
  baskets.
Golden whips glint at the horses' flanks,
Gauze sleeves brush the green boughs.
Racing dawn, the carriages come home,—
And the girls with their high baskets full of fruit.

— *Emperor Ch'ien Wēn-ti*
TRANSLATED BY ARTHUR WALEY

Archibald's Example

Old Archibald, in his eternal chair,
Where trespassers, whatever their degree,
Were soon frowned out again, was looking off
Across the clover when he said to me:

"My green hill yonder, where the sun goes down
Without a scratch, was once inhabited
By trees that injured him—an evil trash
That made a cage, and held him while he bled.

"Gone fifty years, I see them as they were
Before they fell. They were a crooked lot
To spoil my sunset, and I saw no time
In fifty years for crooked things to rot.

"Trees, yes: but not a service or a joy
To God or man, for they were thieves of light.
So down they came. Nature and I looked on,
And we were glad when they were out of sight.

"Trees are like men, sometimes; and that being so,
So much for that." He twinkled in his chair,
And looked across the clover to the place
That he remembered when the trees were there.

– Edwin Arlington Robinson

A Line-Storm Song

The line-storm clouds fly tattered and swift.
    The road is forlorn all day,
Where a myriad snowy quartz stones lift,
    And the hoof-prints vanish away.
The roadside flowers, too wet for the bee,
    Expend their bloom in vain.
Come over the hills and far with me,
    And be my love in the rain.

The birds have less to say for themselves
    In the wood-world's torn despair
Than now these numberless years the elves,
    Although they are no less there:
All song of the woods is crushed like some
    Wild, easily shattered rose.
Come, be my love in the wet woods, come,
    Where the boughs rain when it blows.

There is the gale to urge behind
    And bruit our singing down,
And the shallow waters aflutter with wind
    From which to gather your gown.
What matter if we go clear to the west,
    And come not through dry-shod?

For wilding brooch shall wet your breast
　　The rain-fresh goldenrod.

Oh, never this whelming east wind swells
　　But it seems like the sea's return
To the ancient lands where it left the shells
　　Before the age of the fern;
And it seems like the time when after doubt
　　Our love came back amain.
Oh, come forth into the storm and rout
　　And be my love in the rain.

－ *Robert Frost*

Chapter Two

Listen—I'll say you a
Park in the city, a
Park in the dusk just
As the snow is beginning:
The gray-blue, the sweet-cold, **the**
Whispering rustling.

And

—Do you remember?—
Floor by floor the lights rising
As darkness filled up
The tall wells of the streets
Gigantically ringing the
Small empty park where
The thin snow slid in
As if it would fall
Through the dusk there forever,
Amidst gears', horns' wrangles
Hushing a circle;
The gray-white, the sweet-cold.

Oh

—Now you remember—
How young and unhappy and

Lovely you were
How uselessly in
Love we were; and there
Walking alone in New York in the snow
You had nobody anywhere to see to
Talk to nowhere to go.

– *Winfield Townley Scott*

The Lonely Street

School is over. It is too hot
to walk at ease. At ease
in light frocks they walk the streets
to while the time away.
They have grown tall. They hold
pink flames in their right hands.
In white from head to foot,
with sidelong, idle look—
in yellow, floating stuff,
black sash and stockings—
touching their avid mouths
with pink sugar on a stick—
like a carnation each holds in her hands—
they mount the lonely street.

– William Carlos Williams

The Bait

Come live with mee, and bee my love,
And we will some new pleasures prove
Of golden sands, and cristall brookes:
With silken lines, and silver hookes.

There will the river whispering runne
Warm'd by thy eyes, more than the Sunne;
And there th'inamor'd fish will stay,
Begging themselves they may betray.

When thou wilt swimme in that live bath,
Each fish, which every channell hath,
Will amorously to thee swimme,
Gladder to catch thee, than thou him.

If thou, to be so seene, beest loath
By Sunne, or Moone, thou dark'nest both,
And if my selfe have leave to see,
I need not their light, having thee.

Let others freeze with angling reeds,
And cut their legges with shells and weeds,
Or treacherously poor fish beset,
With strangling snare, or windowie net:

Let coarse bold hands, from slimy nest
The bedded fish in banks out-wrest;
Or curious traitors, sleave-silk flies,
Bewitch poore fishes' wand'ring eyes.

Foe thee, thou need'st no such deceit,
For thou thy selfe art thine owne bait;
That fish, that is not catch'd thereby,
Alas, is wiser far than I.

— *John Donne*

We'll Go No More A-Roving

So, we'll go no more a-roving
    So late into the night,
Though the heart be still as loving,
    And the moon be still as bright.

For the sword outwears its sheath,
    And the soul wears out the breast,
And the heart must pause to breathe,
    And Love itself have rest.

Though the night was made for loving,
    And the day returns too soon,
Yet we'll go no more a-roving
    By the light of the moon.

– Lord Byron

NOT ALL THE POEMS OR POETS in this anthology have been commented on in these notes. Since this book is an invitation to poetry, we can only hope that some of the poems or poets not mentioned in the notes will lead the enterprising young reader to research of his own. We have on the whole tried to avoid the well-worn showpieces of poetry which too often appear in too many anthologies and have tried instead to open the door to new worlds of magic, to poems that will bring a fresh impact on the imagination. Many of the poems in this book are by rare poets who have done beautiful but not too well-known work, and are in need of quiet and individual discovery. Whenever necessary, we have in a note tried to introduce the poet and sometimes explain his work. Some of these notes will, we hope, open new doors and make new discoveries for the reader. The purpose of this book is to lead the reader, whether young or old, to form his own taste; to lead him off the beaten path, and to make him see, as in Blake's "The Crystal Cabinet," how the fields of poetry open always into worlds beyond the visible world. Sometimes knowledge of the life of the poet adds glamour and understanding to his work, and then a note will add heightened interest; often a mere date and fact is enough to lead to further reading, for this book is an invitation to discovery.

Notes

PAGE 1 / "The Crystal Cabinet," to Blake, who was a great mystic, opens itself to a number of interpretations. It may read as the poet's eye of vision opening windows into the invisible world around us; seeing and treating the world beyond the visible world—but the effort is beyond human endurance; the vision is caught and then disappears.

PAGE 7 / Robert Hillyer (1895–1962) was a lyric poet with an exquisite musical ear and unusual technical skill. A popular teacher at Harvard University for many years, where he held the famous Boylston Professorship of Rhetoric, he was a fanatical romantic traditionalist. At his best, his work has charm and elegance and wit, and at times has a similarity to an English poet he much admired—Robert Bridges.

PAGE 11 / Lizette Woodworth Reese (1856–1935) was a Baltimore high-school teacher whose work was much admired at the turn of the century. The popularity of Edna St. Vincent Millay's verse—more colorful, less reticent than Miss Reese's—and the "new poetry" that came in after World War I, dimmed her fame greatly. She had a quaint

194

charm and a language of her own. Her poetry reflects the sights and sounds of a vanishing Baltimore, its eighteenth and early nineteenth century character, and its landscapes, which so much resemble those of the counties of Southern England.

PAGE 14 / This song has a number of different versions. It is probably Scotch (not Irish, as has sometimes been said) and of early twentieth-century origins.

PAGE 16 / William Henry Davies (1870–1940), sometimes known as "the tramp poet," was really a vagabond until George Bernard Shaw discovered him. Coming from a poverty-ridden Welsh family, he made his way to America as a youth, where he earned his way as a panhandler and agricultural day laborer, working at his delicate, racy lyrics during odd moments. Shaw describes him as "a genuine innocent writing odds and ends of verse, about odds and ends of things, living quite out of the world in which such things are usually done . . ."

Davies' naive innocence covered a world of rich observation of people and of nature, and he had an inherent gift of song which at times was truly worthy of Blake. His Welsh heritage crops up in his rich imagination and cadences. When the poetry of the twentieth century is fully evaluated, it may well be that Davies will be placed among the true poets of the century. The poem "Eardrops" in this anthology has a graceful elegance and courtliness that reminds

one of the cavalier-parson poet of the seventeenth century—
Robert Herrick.

PAGE 21 / H. D. (Hilda Doolittle—1886–1962) was an exquisite poet who has always had a devoted if small following. She was always the most fastidious, the least self-exploiting of poets. She lived in a world of her own creation, the world of classical Greece in its full glory, which she made as real as the living world around her. Known for her beauty and wit as a young girl, she traveled widely in Europe and at one time was engaged to the poet Ezra Pound. She became a friend of D. H. Lawrence, who wrote many of his wonderful letters from a London apartment she had turned over to him in his most difficult period.

Her father, Charles L. Doolittle, was professor of astronomy and mathematics at Lehigh University and later became head of the Astronomical Laboratory at the University of Pennsylvania. She studied at Bryn Mawr College where she met the poet Marianne Moore who became a lifelong friend. During this period she also met Ezra Pound and William Carlos Williams, poets who were pioneers in what was beginning to be known as the "new poetry."

Though often linked with the group of poets known as the "Imagists," she really belongs to no school and no group. She learned many things from the brilliant group of poets who were her friends, but her quality of mind and spirit is uniquely her own. Before she died, she published what may well be her masterpiece—a long lyric-narrative poem, "Helen in Egypt"—and a spiritual autobiography disguised

196

as a novel, "Bid Me to Live," which is one of the rarely beautiful books of our time, both for its prose style and its fine perceptions. Ford Madox Ford, the influential novelist and critic, hailed her as the heroine of the imagist movement, saying "She was our gracious Muse, our cynosure and the peak of our achievement."

H. D. died in Switzerland where she had lived for many years. At one time she had been married to Richard Aldington, the English poet and novelist.

PAGE 22 / Ezra Pound (1885–   ), whose stormy career culminated in a trial for treason following World War II, is, like his distant relative, Henry Wadsworth Longfellow, a "culture bearer." He has tried to introduce into American poetry, by means of his fine translations, the literature of many countries, especially those of Europe and Asia. His Chinese translations are particularly felicitous. He is responsible for innovations in the writing of modern poetry, and has opened the way for much of the "new poetry" that has been most influential in the last few decades. Among the writers he first helped to bring to the attention of the public were T. S. Eliot, James Joyce, Robert Frost, and William Carlos Williams. Ezra Pound now lives in Italy.

PAGE 25 / Christina Rossetti (1830–1894) is probably one of the very few first-rate women poets. Her poems have a rare music that is very much her own, delicate and subtle. Of Italian descent, she was the sister of another fine poet (and painter)—Dante Gabriel Rossetti (1828–1882)—who

197

was one of the leaders of the Pre-Raphaelite group in England, and of whom it has been said, "He painted his poems and wrote his pictures." This poem, "An Apple Gathering," has some of the quality of a Pre-Raphaelite illustration. One can see the peaceful rural Victorian landscape, the happy young couples, and the wistful maiden. Christina Rossetti is also known for her deeply-felt religious poems that have an ardent mystical quality found more often in Italian than in English poetry.

PAGE 28 / After Emily Dickinson's (1830–1886) death, the greater body of her uncollected work was left to be edited by devoted friends and relatives who could not always decipher her manuscripts and were often careless. They thought it no harm to touch up her odd spelling and punctuation, and smooth out (what to them were) her rough metrics. In 1955 the Harvard University Press published a scholarly edition of Emily Dickinson's poetry, in three volumes, which kept intact her own metrics, spelling, punctuations, and worked out the different variations of the text of her poems. This very necessary edition was the product of many years of labor on the part of Dr. Thomas H. Johnson of the English department of the Lawrenceville School. The poem we have used in this book was taken from Dr. Johnson's edition of Emily Dickinson's poems.

PAGE 32 / Charles D'Orleans (1391–1465) was a member of the French royal family. He married his cousin, the child queen of Richard II of England, after the latter's death.

Captured at the battle of Agincourt (1415), he was kept a prisoner in England until 1440. He spent his last years at Blois where he gathered around him a circle of poets. His work consists mostly of ballades and rondeaux, the latter a verse form that he made particularly his own. He also wrote some beautiful elegies on the death of his first wife, Isabella of France.

PAGE 32 / Henry Wadsworth Longfellow (1807–1882), besides being a poet of enormous popular appeal and influence (He is the only American poet to be represented by a bust in Westminster Abbey.), was a "culture bearer." Like Ezra Pound, a translator of much unfamiliar poetry, Longfellow introduced to Americans the literature of many cultures, and so widened and enriched the field of knowledge and understanding for the poets who came after him. His translations are of a very high level, introducing poems from the French, Italian, Spanish, German, even Russian and Finnish. ("The Song of Hiawatha" is based on the metrics of the national epic of Finland.) His translation of Dante's "Divine Comedy" is often superb and has rarely been bettered by subsequent translators.

PAGE 35 / John Clare (1793–1864), a contemporary of Shelley, Keats, Wordsworth, Byron, and Coleridge, was not fully appreciated by his contemporaries, and continued unrecognized until almost eighty years after his death. This was due to the unfortunate circumstances of his life, which was crowded with poverty, bad health, uncongenial physical labor, and ultimately, madness. It is now conceded that along with Wordsworth, he was one of the great English poets of nature, full of delicate, minute observations and deep feeling. His notebooks show that he could have taken his place among the important naturalists if time and circumstances had allowed him. His parents were poor farmers and he himself eked out a precarious living as a farm laborer. But somehow he managed to educate himself, and his poetry, occasional prose, and letters have a quiet refinement and sensitivity that make some of his better-known contemporaries seem somewhat vulgar. The strain of his difficulties—literary, domestic, economic—were too much for him, and it is a curious fact that when he went mad, he imagined himself to be the famous, the popular Lord Byron!

PAGE 38 / Hart Crane (1899–1932) is among the best of twentieth-century poets, and his masterpiece, "The Bridge," a symbolic poem about Brooklyn Bridge, has a fire and lyric intensity and richness of expression that improves with each reading. After a life spent in the tragic tradition of Poe and Rimbaud, he committed suicide by jumping overboard from a boat returning to the United States from Mexico. His short poems are noted for their firmness, lyric intensity, and visionary insight.

PAGE 39 / Robert Fitzgerald (1910–   ) is a contemporary American poet living in Italy. He is among the best living translators of Greek poetry and with his friend and collaborator, Dudley Fitts, has done many translations from the Greek dramatists. His most brilliant work in that field is his recent translation of the Odyssey. His poetry has distinction, grace, and verbal felicity.

PAGE 49 / Dr. Lancelot Andrewes (1555–1626) is better known as one of the great theologians of the Anglican Church, where as Bishop of Winchester and a favorite counsellor of James I, he was one of the learned churchmen who helped to translate the King James Version of the Bible. The prose of his sermon is superb; it has won in recent times an eloquent appreciation from T. S. Eliot. A great scholar, a man of austere piety, he often wrote charming verses of which "Phillis Inamorata" is an example.

PAGE 50 / After a poverty-stricken childhood and youth, David Schubert (1913–1946) was awarded a scholarship to Amherst, where he was befriended by a number of professors and by Robert Frost. His poetry appeared in anthologies and magazines, and he was beginning to gain recognition when he died. Schubert's book, *Initial A* (Macmillan 1962), revived interest in his fresh, authentic talent.

PAGE 56 / Thomas Moore (1779–1852), an Irish poet educated at Trinity College, Dublin, was a contemporary of all the great early Romantic poets and was in many ways (with the exception of Lord Byron) the most popular of them all. His "Irish Melodies" were the forerunners of the poems of

Irish nationalism that were to flourish a century later. Handsome, a friend of the Prince Regent and of Byron, he was much in demand as a singer of his own ballads and lyrics in fashionable drawing rooms. His easy, careless lyricism, as exemplified in "The Last Rose of Summer," "The Ministrel Boy," or his overpraised "Lalla Rookh" (an oriental romance), which was set in the Eastern milieu then fashionable, made best sellers of his works. His fame has not grown, but some of his lyrics have a graceful, compelling power and charm. For some reason, his "Lalla Rookh" was considered rather naughty and Lord Byron, reviewing it, spoke of:

> *Lalla Rookh*
> *A naughty book*
> *By Thomas Moore*
> *Who has written four,*
> *Each one*
> *Warmer*
> *Than the former.*

PAGE 65 / Thomas Campion (1567–1620) can be best described as one of the most perfect examples of a poet's poet. A belated Elizabethan, his most characteristic work was done in the reign of James I. He took an active part in producing some of the beautiful court masques (a combination of poetry, pageantry, ballet, and music), and some of his best songs were written for these elaborate festivities in which many great personages took part. His music and diction are the purest and most subtle in English poetry, for since he

202

was a composer and musician as well as a poet, he wrote many of his poems to be sung to the lute, an instrument on which he excelled. Some of his music has been recently rediscovered and performed.

PAGE 67 / Walter Savage Landor (1775–1864), like Thomas Campion, is a true poet's poet, a great classicist, and a writer of vigorous colorful prose. Like Shelley, Byron, or the Sitwells, he came from the landed aristocracy of England and his style has a mixture of eighteenth-century firmness and elegance combined with the passion and color (though restrained) of the Romantics. This is not so strange when one remembers that Landor was born in the age of Dr. Johnson, saw Shelley in his youth, and in his old age received the too excitable (to him) homage of Swineburne. The Brownings, Elizabeth and Robert (his neighbors in Italy), were also his admirers. Landor's poetry and his position in English poetry are unique—he is always being forgotten and rediscovered. William Butler Yeats adopted many of his mannerisms, especially his air of aristocratic pride and arrogance.

PAGE 68 / Robert Duncan (1919–   ), born in Oakland, California, has appeared in what have often been called the "Beatnik" anthologies and publications of what was at one time known as the San Francisco Group.

Mr. Duncan, however, seems to be the least characteristic member of the group and has what few of them have— an imagination and artistry of his own.

<small>PAGE 81 /</small> Rainer Maria Rilke (1875–1926) is one of the great poets of the twentieth century and his influence has been world-wide. His attitude towards poetry and life was unique, though he can perhaps be compared to a great French contemporary in prose, Marcel Proust. Like the latter, he was gifted with a rare sensibility and seemed to put the intangible into music and into words. Rilke's elegance, delicacy, and extraordinary psychological insight made him especially interesting to great ladies of wealth and culture, and he spent many years of his life upheld by their patronage and admiration. There is indeed something in some aspects of his poetry so beautifully feminine that it has been said by one critic that "he wrote the sort of poetry that all women who write poetry would have written if they were great poets." Many English translations have been made of his poetry. The editors of this volume have felt that the translations of C. P. MacIntyre, an American poet living in France, are the best, particularly in the shorter pieces. Rilke, though he traveled widely in many countries and died in Switzerland, was an Austrian by birth and is probably the greatest twentieth-century poet who wrote in German.

<small>PAGE 84 /</small> Anna Akhmatova (1888–   ) is or was (for her fate and whereabouts are now shrouded in silence) one of the most distinguished poets of this century, and one of that rare handful of women who are *poets,* not poetesses. One can best describe her as a kind of Russian Emily

204

Dickinson, mystical, witty, yet not unworldly. For two excellent critical accounts of her work and career, we would like to refer the interested reader to Prince Mirsky's *Contemporary Russian Literature* (Knopf) and Marc Slonim's *Modern Russian Literature* (Oxford University Press). Her religious rather than her political convictions brought her the same treatment from the Soviet arbiters of literature that was given to her contemporary, Boris Pasternak, and her work was withdrawn from circulation and denounced. Less fortunate than Pasternak, her fall from favor passed almost unnoticed in the outside world, and her subsequent career is unknown. At one time Anna Akhmatova was married to Gumilev, one of the most distinguished of the Russian symbolist poets. He was executed in the early days of the Revolution under charges that now seem unconvincing, not to say mysterious.

PAGE 87 / Vittoria Colonna (1492–1547), the subject of this poem, was one of the greatest heroines of the Renaissance, and herself a poet of beauty and interest. Born into the great family of the Colonnas, probably the leading aristocratic family of Rome, she was married at the age of nineteen to Fernando de Ávalos, Marqués de Pescara, a man of culture, and a commander in the service of the Emperor Charles V. While he was away at the wars, Vittoria Colonna corresponded with her husband in prose and verse, and when he was killed in battle in 1525, she wrote many amatory and religious verses in his honor, some of which are among the treasures of Italian literature. After his death, Vittoria Colonna returned to one of her husband's estates in Ischia (the *Inarimé* of this poem by Longfellow). Later she returned to Rome where she became the center of a distinguished group of admirers, among them the English Cardinal Pole, the poet-Cardinal Bembo, and above all, the great sculptor, painter, poet, Michaelangelo. She was probably the one great love of Michaelangelo's life and he commemorated her in a number of his sonnets and lyrics.

PAGE 90 / "Leofric and Godiva" is from a small unfinished fragment of a verse drama that Landor had planned to write about the story of Lady Godiva.

PAGE 91 / The stories and legends about Deirdre are inexhaustible. One may call her the Irish Helen of Troy. She is the unhappy heroine of the ancient Irish epic called "The Fate of the Sons of Uisnech" (Usna) sometimes referred to as "one of the three sorrowful tales of Ireland." There are many different versions of her story, but, like Helen of Troy, she seemed always to be a cause of misfortune to all who loved her.

PAGE 94 / On the anniversary of the founding of Rome it was the custom for a choir of boys and girls to march in procession to the temple of Diana and sing a hymn in honor of the goddess.

PAGE 97 / The early death of James Elroy Flecker (1884–1915), an English poet, leaves critics speculating as to what he might have accomplished if he had lived longer. His was a gifted and attractive personality. A student of Oriental languages, he filled his poems with rather lush oriental imagery, literature, and landscape, which somehow still left his poetry very English and of his day. When he graduated from Oxford, he entered the consular service where he began to make a name for himself. He had many youthful high-sounding theories about poetry, but his poetry was the romantic, lyrical verse of the younger poets of his day, known as "The Georgians," who had revolted against Tennyson and Swinburne, but turned to the philosophical nature poems of Wordsworth, Coleridge, and Hardy. (A revival of the Georgian style of poetry is occurring today in the United States.) The Georgians flourished in England before World War I and under the auspices of Sir Edward Marsh, private secretary to Sir Winston Churchill, published their work in his book-form magazine known as "The Georgian Anthologies," till the war scattered and killed many of them, of whom the best-known was Rupert Brooke.

Flecker developed tuberculosis before the war began and so escaped being a war poet. His work and career interrupted, chafing at being denied the military actions of his friends, he died in a tuberculosis sanitorium at Davos Platz, Switzerland, on January 3, 1915.

PAGE 100 / Hugh MacDiarmid (1892–   ) is one of the colorful characters in twentieth-century poetry. A Scottish nationalist, he was at one time active in a Scottish independence group and in labor movements, and his poems in the Scottish vernacular have been the most popular of their kind since Robert Burns. His *Collected Poems* have been brought out for the first time in this country (Macmillan) and established him as a poet of great but uneven powers. No one since E. E. Cummings has written so many delightful compliments to the opposite sex. "A Pair of Sea-Green Eyes" is a gay bit of "spoofing," and its mock erudition is only part of the fun and is probably a parody on the learned poets of the last decades.

PAGE 109 / C. P. Cavafy (1863–1933), an Alexandrian Greek, was one of the great poets of the beginning of the twentieth century. A native of that colorful (still part European, part Greek, part African) city of Alexandria, he commemorated in his poems the history of his city; its Roman, Greek, Egyptian heritage, its present as well as its past. Alexandria has been called the Paris as well as the New York of the ancient world because of its intellectual, commercial, and artistic activities. It was the capital of Cleopatra's Egypt and in the poem, "Alexandrian Kings," he draws a colorful picture of Cleopatra and her children by Mark Anthony, and her son Caesarion by Julius Caesar, in one of her last public ceremonies. After the death of Mark Anthony and Cleopatra,

Caesarion was put to death by Caesar's nephew, the future emperor Augustus. This was done on the advice of someone who told Augustus "there must not be too many Caesars." Caesarion was then about seventeen years old. Cavafy seems obsessed by Caesarion, who appears in many of his poems. Among the many translations of Cavafy, the Mavrogordato versions are undoubtedly the best.

PAGE 114 / Arthur Gregor (1923–   ) is a young American poet who was born in Vienna and is—what is rare for a poet—an engineer by profession. His two books, *Declension of a Refrain* (1954) and *Octavian Shooting Targets* (1957), are slowly gaining him recognition, because of their dignity, high seriousness, and cosmopolitan atmosphere.

PAGE 118 / Of this poem, the translator poet-novelist Frank O'Connor says, "This is one of the songs of the mad king *Suihhne* (pronounced Sweeney) from a twelfth-century Gaelic romance, the material of which goes back to the eighth century." Of Sweeney, the mad king, the legend goes that he often sat among the trees and learned the language of the birds.

PAGE 119 / This song commemorates one of the sixteenth-century wars in the Low Countries when England helped the Dutch in their fight for independence. It is possible that Kipling took the title for his book, *Soldiers Three,* from this once-popular song. Queen Elizabeth was, it is sad to relate, noted for her parsimony and the picture of the returned soldier, penniless, unemployed, but still cheerful, had its pathos.

PAGE 129 / The Irish airman of Yeats' poem was Major Robert Gregory, who was an aviator in World War I and died in a last engagement in Italy (1918), just before the war's end. He was the only son of Augusta, Lady Gregory, Yeats' patron and friend, and there are many references to him in Yeats' poems. In his great elegy in memory of Major Gregory, Yeats calls up the ghosts of many of his dead friends and says:

> *I am accustomed to their lack of breath*
> *But not that my dear friend's dear son*
> *Our Sidney and our perfect man*
> *Could share in that discourtesy of death.*

The Anne Gregory of the poem on page 15 was his daughter, Lady Gregory's granddaughter.

PAGE 140 / The legend of St. Dorothea is one of the most colorful in the calendar of saints. St. Dorothea, a virgin of noble birth and great beauty, was brought before the Roman governor Theophilus on the charge of being a Christian. Since that was in the period of the greatest Christian persecutions, she was offered the choice of paying homage to the pagan gods or death. Though urged by Theophilus to avoid death by burning incense to the gods and to the

Emperor, she refused and accepted martyrdom, telling Theophilus that she would send a messenger to him after death to prove the validity of the faith. A short time after she had been executed there appeared before Theophilus a child of angelic beauty carrying in his hands a basket of flowers and fruit "the likeness and beauty of which never appeared on earth." Theophilus was convinced. He too became a Christian and also suffered martyrdom.

PAGE 142 / When he died at the age of seventy-three in 1960, Edwin Muir (1887–1960) had been slowly discovered to be one of the leading poets and men of letters of this century. His career had been one of slow recognition and long struggle. His poetry, completely out of the fashions of the day, has a unique quality of its own. Packed with meditative and philosophic thought, his work often shows the influence of Wordsworth. His *Autobiography,* in which he tells the story of his early struggles and his slow rise to fame and influence, is one of the masterpieces of English biography. He was born in Scotland, in the Hebrides, and the landscape of these remote and lonely islands is often reflected in his verse.

PAGE 144 / Born in Essex, England, Ruth Pitter (1897–   ) is one of the finest traditional poets writing in English today. Though not as well-known as she deserves to be in the United States, she has had considerable popularity in her own country. She was the winner of the Hawthornden Prize (the most coveted literary award in England) for her book of poems *Urania* (1950) and of The Queen's Medal for Poetry (1955). Of her poetry the distinguished English critic, Lord David Cecil says, "The firm fastidiousness and nobility of her style is the true mirror of her mind and imagination." William Butler Yeats was one of the admirers of her poetry.

PAGE 145 / Fenton Johnson is a Negro poet born in Chicago who has published a few memorable poems. One wishes he had written more poems like the one published in this anthology, which first appeared in an unusually fine group in *Poetry Magazine,* Chicago. He was born in 1888 and seems to have been lost sight of in recent years. In a biographical note to an anthology of Negro verse edited by Countee Cullen (1927), called *Caroling Dusk,* Mr. Johnson wrote, "My complete autobiography I promise to the world when I am able to realize that I have done something." So perhaps we may hope to hear from Mr. Johnson again!

PAGE 158 / "I mun be married a Sunday" is a lyric from *Ralph Roister Doister,* a popular play by an obscure Elizabethan playwright. The date of the play is uncertain, but is placed about 1550, and even its authorship, usually attributed to Nicholas Udall, is uncertain.

PAGE 181 / A rare treat is before the lover of real poetry who comes across Arthur Waley's *A Hundred and Seventy Chinese Poems,* published in the United States by Knopf

212

(1919). Arthur Waley, an Englishman, has never been surpassed in his translations from the Chinese except occasionally by Ezra Pound. His translations are what all good translations of poetry ought to be—equally excellent as poems in the language in which they are translated. The poem "Lo-yang" was written by an Emperor of China who was also a poet. He lived in the sixth century, A.D.; the dark ages in the Western world, but a period of great civilization and culture in China. "The Golden Palace" is an anonymous picture of civilized Chinese life in the first century of the Christian era.

PAGE 186 / Winfield Townley Scott (1916–   ) is a New England poet who now lives in Santa Fe, New Mexico. His last book of poems *Scrimshaw* (1960) is his best, unpretentious, honest, and full of charm. I know of no poem where the loneliness and bewilderment of sensitive adolescent youth in a large city is so well expressed as in "Chapter Two," his poem in this anthology.

Title Index

(Page numbers referring to notes are in italics.)

Author Index

218

Index of First Lines

222

Horace Gregory is an eminent poet and classical scholar, teacher and critic. His wife, Marya Zaturenska, is a distinguished poet, critic, and biographer. They have collaborated on several anthologies of verse and together they wrote *A History of American Poetry*. The Gregorys have a son and a daughter.

Born in Milwaukee, Mr. Gregory attended the University of Wisconsin of which his grandfather was a founder. He was a professor of Classic Literature and Poetic and Critical Theory for twenty-eight years at Sarah Lawrence College. A translator of Catullus and *The Metamorphoses*, Mr. Gregory is now completing a translation of the love poems of Ovid. He has written a study of D. H. Lawrence and biographies of James McNeill Whistler and Amy Lowell. *Medusa in Gramercy Park* is his most recent collection of poems. Among the many acknowledgments of his talent have been a Guggenheim Fellowship, awards from *Poetry* magazine and the Institute of Arts and Letters, and the Academy of American Poets Award for "distinguished work in American poetry."

Mrs. Gregory was born in Kiev, Russia, of a Russian-Polish family. She is the author of five books of poetry, among them *Terraces of Light, Cold Morning Sky,* and *Selected Poems,* as well as a highly praised biography of Christina Rossetti. *Cold Morning Sky* was awarded the Pulitzer Prize, and she has received numerous other awards for her verse.